Walk Around

F-15 Eagle

By Lou Drendel

Color by Lou Drendel and Don Greer

Illustrated by Andrew Probert

Walk Around Number 28

squadron/signal publications

Introduction

By nearly any measure, the McDonnell Douglas (now Boeing) **F-15 Eagle** is the best fighter ever built. Since entering service in 1974, no F-15 Eagle has been lost to an enemy fighter. On the other hand, Eagles have shot down over 100 of their adversaries. The F-15's attack variant, the **F-15E Strike Eagle,** can carry up to 23,000 pounds (10,432.8 KG) of air-to-ground ordnance and deliver it day or night, fair weather or foul, with unerring accuracy.

The F-15 grew out of the United States Air Force (USAF) Fighter Experimental (FX) proposal of 1965. North American Rockwell, Fairchild-Hiller, and McDonnell Douglas were asked to submit proposals for the new air superiority fighter. McDonnell Douglas was announced as the winner on 23 December 1969. The F-15 prototype made its maiden flight on 22 July 1972. The initial order for production aircraft (**F-15A** single-seat fighters and **TF-15A** – two-seat fighter-trainers) was placed on 1 March 1973. The first production F-15 Eagle was delivered to the USAF's 58th Tactical Fighter Training Wing (TFTW) at Luke Air Force Base (AFB), Arizona on 14 November 1974. The first operational F-15 unit was the 1st Tactical Fighter Wing (TFW) at Langley AFB, Virginia.

An early demonstration of the F-15's capabilities came on 26 August 1974. A TF-15A made a 2660 nautical mile (3063 mile/4929.3 KM) non-stop, unrefueled flight from Loring AFB, Maine to Royal Air Force (RAF) Bentwaters, England. This 5.4-hour flight delivered the aircraft to the Farnborough Air Show. The TF-15A departed Loring at a gross weight of 67,000 pounds (30,391.2 KG), which included 33,000 pounds (14,968.8 KG) of fuel. The fuel load included 19,500 pounds (8845.2 KG) carried in two Fuel And Sensor Tactical (FAST) Packs, conformal fuel tanks attached to the fuselage sides. The FAST Packs – later called Conformal Fuel Tanks (CFTs) – allowed the Eagle to carry additional fuel without the added drag of external tanks.

The impressive transatlantic flight was eclipsed some five months later by the **'Streak Eagle,'** a stripped down F-15A which set eight time-to climb records between 16 January and 1 February 1975. One such record saw the 'Streak Eagle' climb from a standing start to 98,425.2 feet (30,000 M) in 3 minutes 27 seconds. It was an auspicious beginning to what would become a long and successful career. McDonnell Douglas produced 446 F-15A/Bs before production of the **F-15C/D** began in 1979. The latter variant – which carries 2000 pounds (907.2 KG) more internal fuel than the F-15A/B - was produced through 1986.

The F-15 was designed with the lessons of the air war over Vietnam in mind. The Eagle became known as the premier long-range interceptor, but was also armed with short-range missiles and a cannon. In its most publicized air war, the Eagle used all its weapons to post a 33 to 0 advantage over the Iraqi Air Force – once thought to be a formidable foe. The Iraqis were equipped with state of the art Soviet and French fighters, but their poor tactics and training made them little more than targets for the highly trained and motivated USAF F-15 pilots. (Israel Defense Force/Air Force F-15s have run up a 58 to 0 advantage over a variety of Arab air forces, with less publicity.) The F-15's avionics give it a 'look down-shoot down' capability. Its APG-70 radar allows F-15 pilots to pick enemy aircraft out of ground clutter and the long range AIM-7 Sparrow missiles can track targets at low altitudes and at head-on closure rates.

The F-15 Eagle currently serves with the USAF and Air National Guard and the air forces of Israel, Japan, and Saudi Arabia. Over 1500 Eagles of all types have been produced. It has proven to be a remarkably versatile aircraft, equally adept at gaining and maintaining air superiority or conducting all-weather, precision, low altitude deep interdiction strikes. The aircraft is produced by Boeing at St. Louis and (the **F-15J/DJ**) by Mitsubishi Heavy Industries at Nagoya, Japan under license. The production line is guaranteed to remain open past the year 2000, fulfilling orders for 72 **F-15S** aircraft for Saudi Arabia and 25 **F-15I**s for Israel. Both are export versions of the F-15E dual role fighter.

Acknowledgements

Bob Binden
David F. Brown
Ted Carlson/Fotodynamics
Detail & Scale/Bert Kinzey
Kenneth Hare

Nate Leong
Don Logan
Dave Mason
McDonnell Douglas
C.M. Reed

Norman E. Taylor
United States Air Force
 (USAF)
Andre Wilderdijk

ISBN 0-89747-433-3

If you have any photographs of aircraft, armor, soldiers or ships of any nation, particularly wartime snapshots, why not share them with us and help make Squadron/Signal's books all the more interesting and complete in the future. Any photograph sent to us will be copied and the original returned. The donor will be fully credited for any photos used. Please send them to:

Squadron/Signal Publications, Inc.
1115 Crowley Drive
Carrollton, TX 75011-5010

Если у вас есть фотографии самолётов, вооружения, солдат или кораблей любой страны, особенно, снимки времён войны, поделитесь с нами и помогите сделать новые книги издательства Эскадрон/Сигнал ещё интереснее. Мы переснимем ваши фотографии и вернём оригиналы. Имена приславших снимки будут сопровождать все опубликованные фотографии. Пожалуйста, присылайте фотографии по адресу:

Squadron/Signal Publications, Inc.
1115 Crowley Drive
Carrollton, TX 75011-5010

軍用機、装甲車両、兵士、軍艦などの写真を所持しておられる方は いらっしゃいませんか？どの国のものでも結構です。作戦中に撮影されたものが特に良いのです。Squadron/Signal社の出版する刊行物において、このような写真は内容を一層充実し、興味深くすることができます。当方にお送り頂いた写真は、複写の後お返しいたします。出版物中に写真を使用した場合は、必ず提供者のお名前を明記させて頂きます。お写真は下記にご送付ください。

Squadron/Signal Publications, Inc.
1115 Crowley Drive
Carrollton, TX 75011-5010

(Front Cover) A McDonnell Douglas F-15C Eagle (79-0048) is parked on the ramp at Bitburg Air Base (AB), Germany during the 1980s. The aircraft was assigned to the 525th Tactical Fighter Squadron (TFS), 36th Tactical Fighter Wing (TFW). The Wing converted from F-4 Phantoms to F-15s in 1977 and provided the primary air defense for southern Germany throughout the late Cold War period.

(Previous Page) An F-15A Eagle (76-0050) of the 53rd TFS, 36th TFW from Bitburg AB, Germany is parked at Pferdsfeld, Germany on 10 December 1979. A 610 gallon (2309.1 L) fuel tank is mounted under the fuselage and rails for AIM-9 Sidewinder Air-to-Air Missiles (AAMs) are installed on the wing pylons.

(Back Cover) A 525th TFS F-15C stands alert in a hardened shelter at Incirlik AB, Turkey during Operation DESERT STORM in early 1991. This Eagle downed one Iraqi aircraft during the Gulf War. The 36th TFW also sent its 53rd TFS to Tabuk AB, Saudi Arabia for the Coalition campaign to liberate Kuwait.

(Above) This F-15A-20-MC (77-0122) is assigned to the 49th TFW at Holloman Air Force Base (AFB), New Mexico. The Eagle is fitted with a 610 gallon centerline fuel tank, which is usually retained during air combat maneuvers. The Wing insignia is applied to the intake trunking immediately aft of the engine intake, while the Tactical Air Command (TAC) insignia appears on the upper vertical tail surfaces. The 49th TFW (49th FW from October of 1991) flew the F-15A from October of 1977 until 1992. The Wing now operates the Lockheed Martin F-117A Nighthawk 'stealth fighter.'

(Right) The access doors and panels are opened up on this F-15A (76-0043) at McDonnell Douglas' St. Louis, Missouri plant. The Eagle has 570 square feet (52.9 M^2) of access covers, with approximately half of these quick access doors. The F-15 has less than half the fasteners found on the earlier F-4 Phantom II, although having a greater number of access panels. The Eagle has 106 'black boxes' (avionics equipment), 97 fuel system plumbing connections, 202 lubrication points, and a projected 11.3 Maintenance Man-Hours per Flight Hour (MMH/FH). The equivalent figures for the Phantom were 294, 281, 510, and 24, respectively. (McDonnell Douglas)

The starboard avionics bay door is opened on this F-15A. The liquid oxygen container mounted in the box supplies breathing oxygen for the pilot. Avionics hardware and bay cooling equipment are placed within easy reach of maintenance personnel. Most F-15 avionics components consist of Line Replaceable Units (LRUs), which allow for easy replacement of the 'black boxes.' (Dave Mason)

The pilot access ladder is attached to the F-15A's port side canopy sill. This ladder is standard for all Eagles. The national insignia applied to F-15A through D models lacked the blue trim to the white and red bars. Black or gray outline national insignia later became standard on all air superiority Eagles. (Lou Drendel)

Access covers on the F-15A are secured to the airframe using either flush screws for removable panels or flush fasteners for doors. Easy maintenance access was one of the Eagle's design concepts, which allowed the F-15 to have a substantially lower MMH/FH than earlier front line fighters. The system of access panels remained little changed for all subsequent F-15 variants. (McDonnell Douglas)

McDonnell Douglas technicians opened the access covers on this F-15A at St. Louis. The large number and size of these covers – comprising both doors and removable panels – allow easy systems maintenance. The radome opens to starboard to reveal the Hughes AN/APG-63 radar antenna. The radar components were accessed through upward-hinged doors on the port and starboard sides. Nose and main wheels were painted Gloss Black (FS17038) on early F-15s before the color was changed to the same Gloss White (FS17875) used on the landing gear struts and bays. (McDonnell Douglas)

The F-15A/B and early C/D Eagles were equipped with the APG-63 pulse-Doppler radar, optimized for air-to-air combat. It is the first functional 'look-down, shoot-down' radar, able to track aircraft flying at low altitude. Data from the APG-63 was filtered to remove ground clutter before it was displayed on a television (TV) screen in the cockpit. This allows the pilot to more easily acquire his targets. (McDonnell Douglas)

Projections along the radar antenna perimeter are air-to-air interrogators, which sends coded radio signals for Selective Identification Feature (SIF), high confidence identification, and Air Traffic Control (ATC) altitude reporting. The radar can search ranges from ten miles (16.1 KM) to 160 miles (257.5 KM) and track high speed targets at high closure rates. The AN/APG-70 radar fitted to later F-15C/D/E aircraft retains the APG-63's antenna. (McDonnell Douglas)

5

(Above) Two F-15As (76-0098 and 76-0091) of the 318th Fighter Interceptor Squadron (FIS) cruise past Mount Rainier in Washington State. The Squadron was based at McCord AFB, Washington. The Eagles are not equipped with 610 gallon (2309.1 L) centerline fuel tanks, which indicates this was a short range training flight. The 318th FIS was one of four ADTAC (Air Defense/Tactical Air Command) squadrons equipped with F-15As for air defense. This Squadron displayed light blue and black rays emanating from a white disc on the tail, with the TAC insignia inside the disc. The 318th flew Eagles from June of 1983 until it was disbanded in October of 1989.

(Left) Two F-15A-17-MCs (76-0104 and 76-0109) of the 48th FIS form up on a third Eagle along the US Atlantic coast. The fighters are armed with four AIM-7 Sparrow air-to-air missiles (AAMs) on the lower fuselage and four AIM-9 Sidewinder AAMs on the wing pylons. The Squadron operated from Langley AFB, Virginia alongside the 1st Tactical Fighter Wing's F-15s. Tail chevrons and rudder stripes were white and medium blue. The 48th had a long history as an Aerospace Defense Command (ADC; later ADTAC) squadron, converting from the Convair F-106 Delta Dart in 1982. The 48th was deactivated in the post-Cold War drawdown of the early 1990s. (USAF via Norman E. Taylor collection)

6

This F-15A (73-109) is assigned to the 122nd FS, 159th Fighter Group (FG) of the Louisiana Air National Guard (ANG). The Squadron flies from Naval Air Station (NAS) New Orleans. The tail band is dark blue with a white *fleur de lis* and border. Louisiana is written in black script below the tail band. (Kenneth Hare)

A 325th FW F-15A (74-132) is displayed at an airbase. Covers are placed over the port engine intake and forward fuselage sensors. The Wing – designated the 325th Tactical Training Wing before August of 1991 – is based at Tyndall AFB, Florida and trains pilots on air-superiority Eagles. (Kenneth Hare)

A 58th TFS F-15A (75-0045) flies on a training mission from Eglin AFB, Florida. The Squadron – part of the 33rd TFW – has blue tail bands on the outboard tail surfaces. A gray eagle's head appears on the black band found on the inner vertical stabilizer surfaces. The 33rd TFW flew F-15A/B models from Eglin from 1979 until October of 1984, when they converted to the later F-15C/D aircraft. (Bob Binden)

This F-15A (77-0117) was assigned to the 8th TFS, 49th TFW at Holloman AFB, New Mexico. The Squadron used yellow tail bands on their Eagles. This aircraft is armed with the standard air superiority weapons fit of AIM-7 Sparrows and AIM-9 Sidewinders. The Wing received its first Eagles in October of 1977 and was the longest-serving F-15A/B wing in the USAF before transitioning to the F-117A in 1992. (Bob Binden)

7

The F-15A instrument panel used analog instruments, with a Head-Up Display (HUD) mounted atop the instrument shroud. The HUD is the heart of a sophisticated avionics and weapons control system. This system uses the Hands on Throttle and Stick (HOTAS) philosophy, which places the essential radar and weapons controls at the pilot's fingertips. (Dave Mason)

The only 'glass' display in the F-15A instrument panel is the Vertical Situation Display (VSD) radarscope to port of the HUD controls. The control stick grip is the same type used by the earlier McDonnell Douglas F-4 Phantom II. F-15 cockpit interiors are Dark Gull Gray (FS36231) with black instrument bezels. (Dave Mason)

An avionics bay is located immediately aft of the F-15A cockpit. The hydraulic canopy actuator was fitted to the aft bulkhead. Cockpit pressurization valves were located atop the aft bulkhead. The bay is painted a light metallic blue-green (approximately FS14241). (Dave Mason)

Line Replaceable Units (LRUs) inside the F-15A avionics bay allow easy replacement by maintenance crews. AN/ALQ-135 Internal Countermeasures Sets (ICS) placed along the port wall provide the Eagle with self contained Electronic Countermeasures (ECM) support. Circuit breaker panels are located on the starboard side. (Dave Mason)

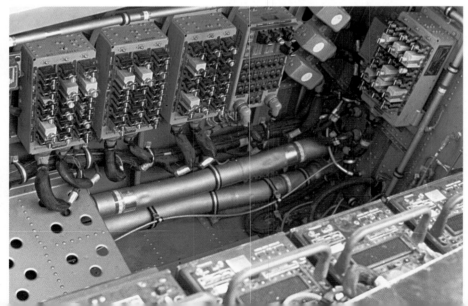

This F-15A-20-MC (77-0132) was assigned to the commander of the 32nd Fighter Group at Camp New Amsterdam, Soesterberg, Netherlands in 1994. The Group (formerly the 32nd TFS) flew F-15A/Bs from September of 1978 until June of 1980, when they transitioned to F-15C/Ds. The unit then received Multi-Stage Improvement Program (MSIP) F-15A/Bs in late 1991. (Via Norman E. Taylor collection)

This F-15A was uniquely marked to celebrate the 40th anniversary of operations as one of the primary North Atlantic Treaty Organization (NATO) air superiority units in Europe. The name of the 32nd FG's commander, Col Bill 'Hodge' Hodgkins, was painted above the Group's nickname, WOLFHOUNDS. The 32nd FG was a USAFE unit, but came under the operational control of the Royal Netherlands Air Force. (Via Norman E. Taylor collection)

The 32nd FG Commander's F-15A (77-1032) received non-standard serial presentation with the CR tail code for Soesterberg. An AN/ALQ-128 Electronic Countermeasures (ECM) pod was fitted atop the port vertical stabilizer, with the AN/ALR-56 Radar Warning Receiver (RWR) immediately below. A position light was placed under the AN/ALR-56 unit. The orange tailband includes a green outlined crown and trim. (Via Norman E. Taylor collection)

The F-15A canopy is hinged at the aft end and opens upward. The canopy closely fit the cockpit sill when closed. A protective cover is draped over the air conditioning exhaust duct immediately aft of the canopy. The blade antenna behind the duct serves the Ultra High Frequency/Very High Frequency (UHF/VHF) radio equipment. (Dave Mason)

The wing neatly blends into the F-15A's upper fuselage. The intake duct bleed air louvers are mounted inboard of the air refueling receptacle. Excess air from the engine intake is vented out of the aircraft through these louvers. The Eagle's wing area of 608 square feet (56.5 m²) allows low speed flying at high angles of attack. (Dave Mason)

The port aileron has drooped, due to the bleeding off of hydraulic pressure minutes after the engines have shut down. Each F-15 aileron measures 26.48 square feet (2.5 m²) in area and travels +/-20˚. The Eagle's control surfaces are built of aluminum honeycomb for lightness and strength. A fuel jettison pipe is mounted immediately outboard of the aileron. (Dave Mason)

The F-15A's horizontal stabilizers are all-moving surfaces, mounted on pivot fitted to the aft fuselage. These stabilizers are identical and are interchangeable for either the port or starboard side. Movement range of the stabilizers in the elevator mode is +/- 20˚. The stabilizers droop without hydraulic pressure being fed into them. (Dave Mason)

A 36th Tactical Fighter Wing (TFW) F-15A is parked at Bitburg Air Base (AB), Germany. A cockpit access ladder is mounted on the port side and two ground service carts are parked beside the aircraft. The Wing converted from F-4 Phantoms to the Eagle in 1977. During the Cold War, it had the primary responsibility of air defense on Europe's central front. (Andre Wilderdijk)

Speed Brake Interior
(All F-15 Production Variants)

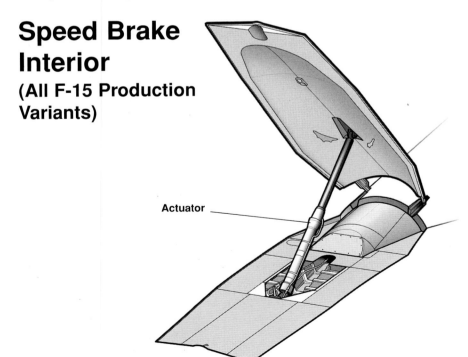

Actuator

The 12th F-15A prototype (72-114) rests at Nellis AFB, Nevada on 3 February 1976. The original 20 square foot (1.9 M^2) speed brake caused buffeting problems when fully extended. This was replaced on the first production aircraft (73-108) with a 31.5 square foot (2.9 M^2) brake, which requires a smaller angle for full deployment. (Don Logan)

This F-15B-8-MC (73-112) of the 128th TFS, 116th TFW, Georgia Air National Guard is parked at London, Ontario, Canada in 1989. This Eagle – the 44th production aircraft – has the later 31.5 square foot (2.9 M^2) speed brake fitted to production F-15s. Engine air intakes are fully lowered to the optimum angle for air induction at steep climb angles. (David F. Brown)

11

An F-15B (76-0135) of the 325th TFW is parked at McCarran International Airport, Las Vegas, Nevada on 17 October 1993. The Eagle is assigned to the Air Defense Training Center at Tyndall AFB, Florida. The F-15B canopy is slightly bulged at the aft end to accommodate the rear seat crewman's head. (Ted Carlson/Fotodynamics)

The F-15B rear seat occupies the avionics bay area found on single-seat F-15As. This Eagle was fitted with the McDonnell Douglas ACES II ejection seat, which replaced the company's Escapac IC-7 seats fitted to early F-15A/Bs through Block 16. (Dave Mason)

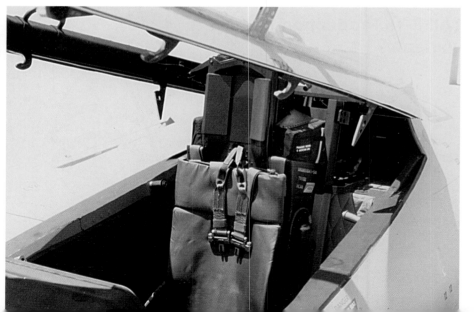

Capt Jim 'Tony' Mahoney boards an F-15B of the 8th TFS, 49th TFW at Holloman AFB in May of 1984. The top of the ladder grabs the cockpit sill, while a padded support section rests against the fuselage side. Locking hooks along the canopy sill engage the cockpit sill to seal the canopy. The 49th TFW was the last USAF unit to operate the F-15A/B and transitioned to the F-117A Nighthawk in 1992. (Lou Drendel)

A metal bar is mounted over the rear instrument panel shroud on the F-15B. This bar is grabbed by the GIB ('Guy In Back;' nickname for rear seat occupants) to aid in entering and leaving the aft cockpit. Instrument shrouds and canopy sills are painted flat Instrument Black (FS37038) to reduce cockpit glare. (Dave Mason)

The F-15B aft instrument panel contains fewer instruments than the forward panel. The Vertical Situation Display (VSD) is mounted in the upper port section, with the main communications control panel to the right. Flight instruments are placed at the center and engine and fuel indicators to starboard. The later F-15D aft instrument panel is virtually identical. (Detail & Scale Photo by Bert Kinzey)

The USAF 'bailed' (loaned) the second F-15B prototype (71-291) to McDonnell Douglas for demonstrator use. This aircraft was the prototype for the 'Strike Eagle,' a company funded proposal for a dual-role (air-to-air and air-to-surface) fighter. The Eagle received an overall 'European I' camouflage of Dark Green (FS34092), Light Green (FS34102), and Dark Gray (FS36081). (McDonnell Douglas)

The F-15B-4 (71-291) flies low over the Mississippi River near McDonnell Douglas' St. Louis plant. Mk 7 Rockeye Cluster Bomb Units (CBUs) are fitted to the 'Strike Eagle's Conformal Fuel Tanks (CFTs) and wing pylon stations, while Sidewinders are mounted on the wing pylons. Aircraft 71-291 served as the F-15E prototype. (McDonnell Douglas)

This 18th TFW F-15C-23-MC (78-0538) appears at Tyndall AFB, Florida on 14 October 1982. The Eagle flew in from Kadena AB, Okinawa for the William Tell Air Defense Competition. William Tell is held every two years for USAF, ANG, and Canadian Forces fighter units. Upper tail chevrons are (forward-aft) blue, yellow, and red – respectively, the colors of the 44th, 12th, and 67th TFS. The mask of the *shogun* (military ruler of ancient Japan) appears on the inner vertical tail surfaces. The tailcode ZZ and the serial number are black, with the last three digits (538) in black on the nose. Insignias of the three squadrons were applied to the starboard intake trunking. No external stores are carried by this aircraft. The 18th TFW was the first F-15C/D unit, receiving their initial Eagles in July of 1979. (Norman E. Taylor)

Two 32nd TFS F-15Cs – including 79-0019, a Block 25 aircraft – fly over Holland in 1982. The Squadron replaced their earlier F-15As with F-15Cs in June of 1980. Both Eagles are armed with the then standard air-to-air missile load of four wing-mounted AIM-9 Sidewinder heat-seeking missiles and four fuselage-mounted AIM-7 Sparrow radar-guided missiles. The 610 gallon (2309.1 L) fuel tank mounted on the centerline pylon gives the F-15C a range of 2500 miles (4023.3 KM), which can be extended through in-flight refueling. The Eagle's lower aft fuselage is left in natural titanium, since paint on this area would flake off due to engine-generated heat. 'Turkey feathers' (nozzle actuator covers) were removed from many F-15s during the early 1980s, due to maintenance problems these parts posed. (USAF via Norman E. Taylor)

Two F-15Cs (80-0030 and 80-0040) of the 57th Fighter Interceptor Squadron escort a Soviet Tupolev Tu-95RTs (Bear-D) reconnaissance and Electronic Intelligence (ELINT) aircraft. The 57th was based at Keflavik Naval Station, Iceland and had primary responsibility for patrolling the GIUK (Greenland-Iceland-United Kingdom) gap during the Cold War. Both Eagles operated with CFTs and were each armed with two AIM-7 Sparrows. (USAF)

An F-15C of the 71st TFS, 1st TFW prepares to taxi before a CAP (Combat Air Patrol) mission from Dhahran, Saudi Arabia in late 1990. The Eagles were the first US fighters deployed to Saudi Arabia, flying non-stop from their home at Langley AFB, Virginia to Dhahran on 7 August 1990. The 6500 mile (10,460.5 KM) flight took 14 hours and required seven aerial refuelings.

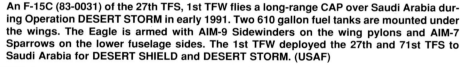

An F-15C (83-0031) of the 27th TFS, 1st TFW flies a long-range CAP over Saudi Arabia during Operation DESERT STORM in early 1991. Two 610 gallon fuel tanks are mounted under the wings. The Eagle is armed with AIM-9 Sidewinders on the wing pylons and AIM-7 Sparrows on the lower fuselage sides. The 1st TFW deployed the 27th and 71st TFS to Saudi Arabia for DESERT SHIELD and DESERT STORM. (USAF)

In May of 1998, this F-15C (82-0024) of the 94th Fighter Squadron, 1st Fighter Wing (FW) was displayed at Andrews AFB, Maryland. The Wing's insignia is placed on the starboard fuselage side, while the Air Combat Command (ACC) badge is applied to the upper vertical stabilizer. A black eagle is painted on the inner vertical stabilizer surfaces. (Lou Drendel)

16

East Coast F-15 display pilot Capt Matt Beals flew this F-15C (83-0017) at Andrews AFB in May of 1998. The Eagle was assigned to the 71st FS, 1st FW (formerly TFW). The Squadron insignia appears on the port fuselage side. A green star above the light yellow nose flush light strip indicated the Iraqi Mirage F.1 downed by Capt Steve Tate in this Eagle on 17 January 1991 – the first day of Operation DESERT STORM. (Lou Drendel)

The name of the F-15's pilot, Capt Matt Beals, is painted in a box on the port nose under the windshield. An eagle's head is placed at the front of the crew box. An identical box on the starboard side has the crew chief's name. Above the light yellow night formation reference light stripe is a green star. The star – trimmed in black with the white lettering MIRAGE F.1 – represents Capt Tate's Iraqi aircraft 'kill' while flying this aircraft on 17 January 1991. (Lou Drendel)

A 3rd Wing F-15C is parked at its home, Elmendorf AFB, Alaska, in 2001. Red protective covers are placed over the pitot tube (front) and Angle of Attack (AOA) probe (aft) on the nose. The runway arrestor hook lowered to the ground snares cables stretched across the runway in the event of a brake failure. The Eagle is finished in the current 'Mod Eagle' scheme of Dark Gray (FS37176) and Light Gray (FS36251) (Lou Drendel)

GULF SPIRIT and the Florida map is applied to the nose of this F-15C (85-0108) assigned to the 58th TFS, 33rd TFW. The Wing is based at Eglin AFB in the Florida panhandle, near the Gulf of Mexico. The crew block contains the name of the Eagle's pilot, Col Greg Martin. The green star edged in black contained MIG 29 in white. This represents an Iraqi MiG-29 downed by Capt R.R. Draeger while flying the F-15C on 17 January 1991. (Ted Carlson/Fotodynamics)

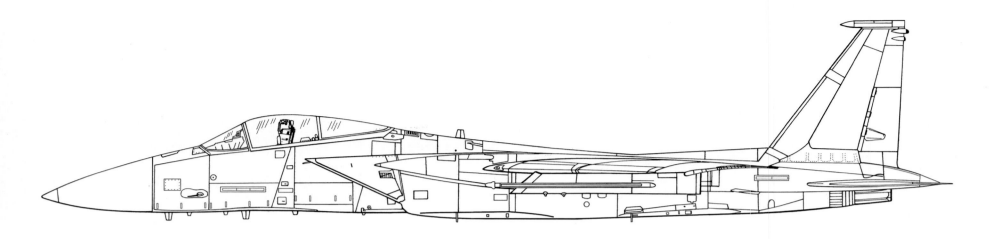

F-15D Forward Fuselage

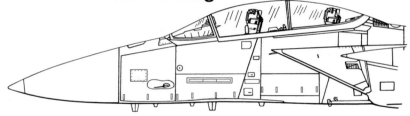

McDonnell Douglas (now Boeing) F-15C Eagle Specifications

Wingspan:............42 feet 9.75 inches (13 м)
Length:..................63 feet 9 inches (19.4 м)
Height:..................18 feet 5.5 inches (5.6 м)
Empty Weight:.......28,600 pounds (12,973 кɢ)
Maximum Weight:..68,000 pounds (30,844.8 кɢ)
Powerplant:...........Two 23,450 pound thrust Pratt & Whitney
  F-100-PW-220 afterburning turbofan engines
Armament:.............One 20мм M61A-1 Vulcan cannon with 940
  rounds; up to four AIM-9 Sidewinder Air-to-Air
  Missiles (AAMs); up to four AIM-7 Sparrow
  AAMs or AIM-120 AMRAAMs

Maximum Speed:..1650 мрн (2655.3 кмн) at 36,000 feet
  (10,972.8 м)
Service Ceiling:.....60,000 feet (18,288 м)
Range:....................2878 miles (4631.6 км) with external fuel tanks;
  3450 miles (5552.1 км) with Conformal Fuel
  Tanks
Crew:.......................One

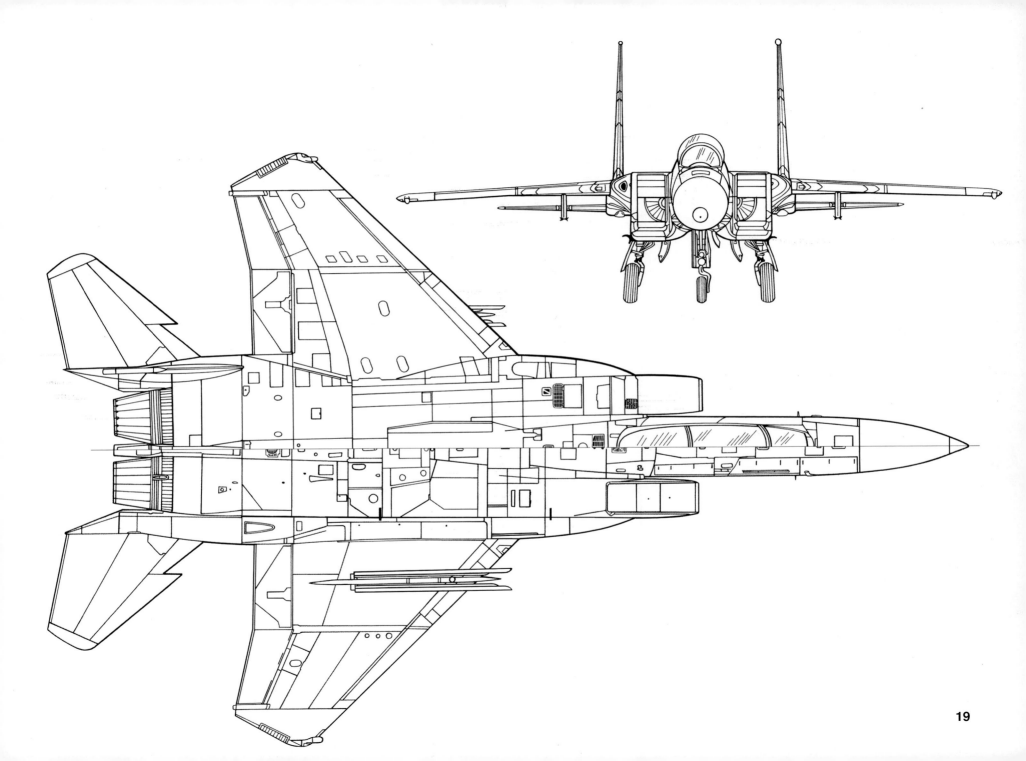

19

The antennas on the F-15C's nose undersurface are for (fore-aft): the UHF (Ultra High Frequency) radio; ECM (Electronic Countermeasures); and the TACAN (Tactical Air Navigation) system. The TACAN antenna exchanged radio signals with ground stations to aid the pilot in navigation. A blue plastic sheet cover was placed over the port engine intake. (Dave Mason)

Three mirrors for rear vision assistance are mounted in the forward canopy frame. Yellow lock/shoot lights are fitted beside the port and starboard mirrors. They steadily light up when there is radar lock on an opposing aircraft and flash when the F-15 pilot is within missile firing parameters. Immediately port of the center mirror is the green air refueling ready light. A standby magnetic compass is mounted starboard of the center mirror. A canopy handgrip is mounted on the lower starboard frame; an identical handgrip is placed on the port side. (C.M. Reed)

The crew access ladder is placed on the port side of an F-15C. It is often used in place of the retractable boarding ladder fitted to all Eagles. Strips of non-slip material are placed on the ladder rungs for easy gripping by hands and booted feet. Lower nose access panel latches are unlocked for maintenance crew access. (Lou Drendel)

A 32nd Tactical Fighter Squadron (TFS) F-15C (79-0042) climbs out shortly after takeoff from Soesterberg AB, the Netherlands. The pilot turns his head to face his leader. The birdstrike-resistant windshield consists of a center polycarbonate layer surrounded by inner and outer layers of fusion bonded cast acrylic. The polycarbonate canopy is made in two sections, separated by a thin red (approximately FS31302) frame. The canopy mate- rial is 0.29 inches (0.74 CM) thick and is covered by an abrasion resistant covering. The Eagle's engine intakes are fully lowered to maximize airflow into the engines during take- off. Most of the 32nd TFS insignia has worn away from the port fuselage side. (McDonnell Douglas via Norman E. Taylor collection)

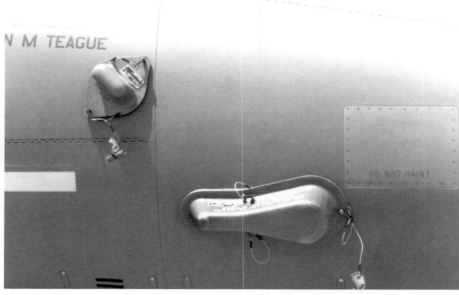

The canopy is open on GULF SPIRIT, an F-15C (85-0103) assigned to the 33rd FW (TFW before late 1991) at Eglin AFB, Florida. A removable brace was placed over the canopy actuator rod aft of the seat. The brace holds open the canopy for extended periods. The internal crew access ladder is lowered on the port side. This Eagle was displayed at Shaw AFB, South Carolina on 8 November 1995. (Norman E. Taylor)

The liquid oxygen (LOX) supply access door is mounted on the starboard side of the nose. The F-15 holds 2.64 gallons (10 L) of liquid oxygen for pilot breathing at high altitudes. The LOX is pressurized at 30 pounds per square inch (PSI). Two flush latches secure the upward-hinged LOX access hatch in place. (Lou Drendel)

Red plastic covers are placed over the Angle of Attack (AOA) probe (aft) and the pitot tube (forward) on an F-15's starboard side. The covers protected the sensitive instruments from damage while the aircraft was on the ground between flights. Red REMOVE BEFORE FLIGHT streamers can be attached to clips fitted to the covers. (Lou Drendel)

A REMOVE BEFORE FLIGHT streamer is attached to covers placed over the AOA sensor on the port side. Protective covers are also fitted to the UHF (forward) and TACAN (aft) antennas. Aft of the formation light strip is the access door for the emergency canopy jettison handle. This handle is used to jettison the canopy if the pilot cannot do so during a ground emergency. (Lou Drendel)

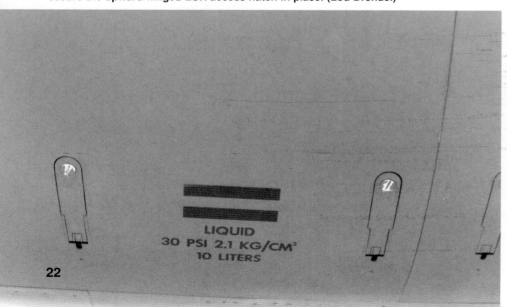

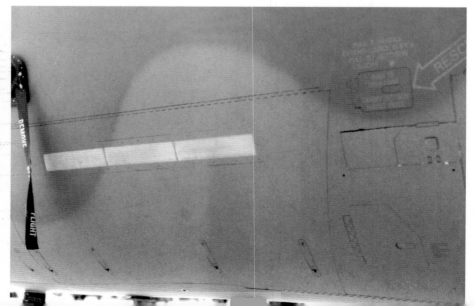

An alternative pitot tube cover is used on this F-15C. The cover consists of thick red vinyl material sewn to form a close fitting cover over the tube. The red flag with REMOVE BEFORE FLIGHT in white reminded ground crewmen to remove the cover before engine start. The pitot tube collects air to feed into the aircraft's airspeed indicator. (Lou Drendel)

A cover with a REMOVE BEFORE FLIGHT streamer is placed over the AOA sensor mast. This mast – above and aft of the pitot tube on both port and starboard sides – senses the aircraft's attitude to relative wind. (Dave Mason)

(Above) A Sperry Multi-Purpose Color Display (MPCD) is fitted to the port side of an F-15C instrument panel. It displays the availability and status of the Eagle's weapons. Buttons surrounding the display screen control the weapons, sensors, and data presented on the screen. The red button at the MPCD's lower left jettisons all external stores in an emergency. The MPCD replaced the earlier armament control panel on F-15C/Ds put through the Multi-Stage Improvement Program II (MSIP-II) during the mid-1980s. (Lou Drendel)

(Left) The F-15C instrument panel is virtually identical to the panel used by the earlier F-15A. The McDonnell Douglas Electronics Head-Up Display (HUD) is mounted atop the instrument shroud. It projects basic flight information onto the combining glass at the pilot's eye level. The HUD controls are mounted below the combining glass. This panel also includes controls for tuning the Identification Friend or Foe (IFF) transponder and the primary communications radio. The Vertical Situation Display (VSD) to port of the HUD control panel displays radar images. The Tactical Electronic Warfare System (TEWS) display unit is located starboard of the control panel. (Lou Drendel)

(Above) Traditional analog flight instruments are used extensively on the F-15C instrument panel. The earlier F-15A/B and the F-15D also used these instruments. The center panel contains the attitude direction indicator above the horizontal situation indicator. The airspeed/Mach indicator is placed immediately below the VSD on the port instrument panel section. The altimeter is located starboard of the attitude direction indicator. Engine and fuel indicators are fitted on the starboard panel section. F-15 cockpits are predominantly Dark Gull Gray (FS36231) and Instrument Black (FS37038). (Lou Drendel)

(Above Right) This F-15C's control stick is fitted with the same grip used in the later F-15E. The red weapon's release button was mounted on the left of the upper stick grip section. Beside the weapon's release is the castle switch, used to cycle (reset) the cockpit displays. The far right button is depressed to dispense chaff and flares used to counter approaching missiles. Moving it left, right, up, or down adjusts the flight trim. The caution lights panel is fitted to the far right instrument panel section, near the right console front. (Lou Drendel)

(Right) The F-15A through D models use the same Head-Up Display (HUD). The combining glass is angled to present vital flight and target information to the pilot at his eye level. This information includes the indicated airspeed, pressure altitude, and magnetic heading. The HUD field of vision is approximately 20° by 20°. (Lou Drendel)

25

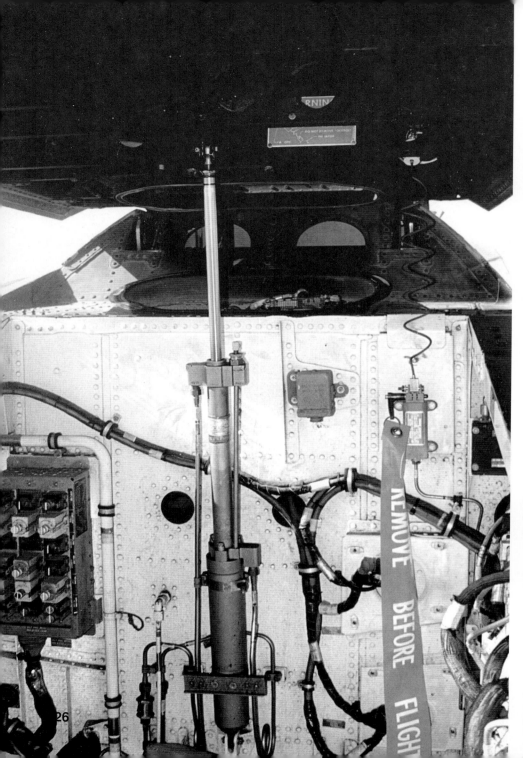

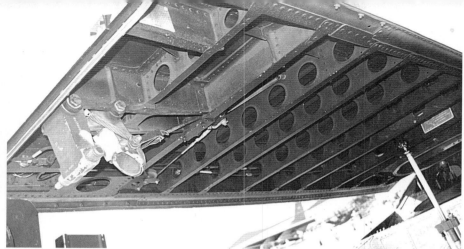

(Above) Ribs support the canopy deck of single-seat F-15s. The deck is painted Instrument Black (FS37038) on both upper and lower surfaces. Lightening holes were placed on the undersurface ribs to reduce weight. The canopy lock mechanism is placed at the deck's front, while the actuating rod is fitted aft. (Lou Drendel)

(Left) The F-15C canopy actuator is mounted on the aft bulkhead of the avionics bay. The hydraulic actuating rod has fully extended to raise the canopy. A red REMOVE BEFORE FLIGHT streamer is attached to the canopy actuated initiator lanyard, which fires the seat when the canopy is jettisoned. Two round cockpit pressurization valves are fitted near the canopy hinge. (Lou Drendel)

(Below) Fittings for the Tactical Electronic Warfare System (TEWS) are mounted on the starboard wall of the F-15C avionics bay. The TEWS consolidates the Eagle's electronic warfare equipment in one location for ease of maintenance and replacement. Various aircraft covers are placed in the avionics bay while the Eagle undergoes maintenance. (Lou Drendel)

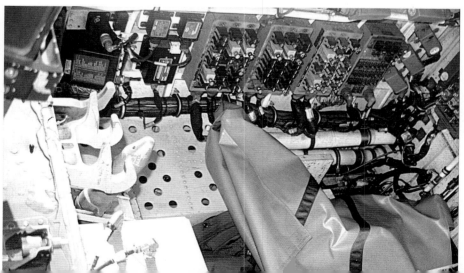

The F-15C canopy locking mechanism is located at the avionics bay front area. This device captures the canopy lock mechanism located on the canopy deck undersurface. A rounded tip rod connects with the lock mechanism socket. The two hooks near the rod engage both lock mechanism rods. The canopy locking system secures the canopy to the fuselage. (Lou Drendel)

The McDonnell Douglas ACES (Advanced Concept Ejection Seat) II seat back rests against the cockpit aft bulkhead. The light colored tube running through the seat back is the rocket motor for ejecting the seat out of the aircraft. Two cross pieces are attached to a brace fitted to the seat rails, which are attached to the cockpit floor. (Lou Drendel)

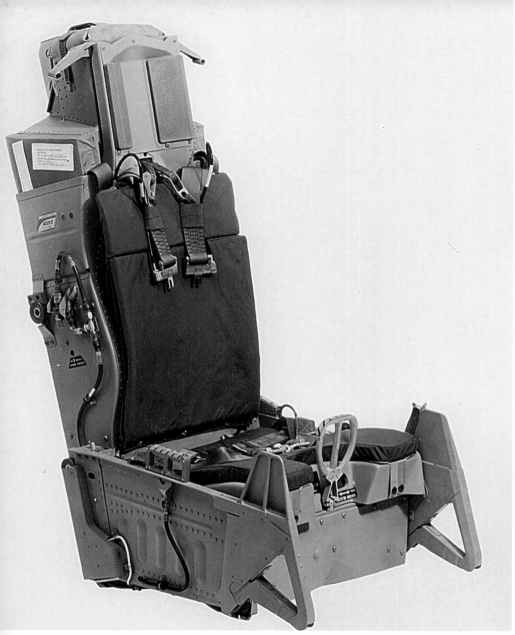

The ACES II ejection seat is used by all F-15s (except Israel's, which use the Escapac IC-7) beginning with F-15A Block 17 aircraft. Barostat sensors are mounted on 'horns' placed on the seat top. The sensors automatically separate the pilot from the seat and deploy his parachute below 15,000 feet (4572 M). This early ACES II has a yellow ejection trigger handle in the seat front center. Most production seats have two ejection control handles at the forward sides. (McDonnell Douglas)

An ACES II seat is fitted to the cockpit of an F-15C. The point at the top of the headrest serves as a canopy breaker in case the canopy does not separate during the ejection sequence. The recovery parachute is located immediately behind the headrest. Emergency oxygen for the pilot is supplied from a green bottle fitted to the port side. (Lou Drendel)

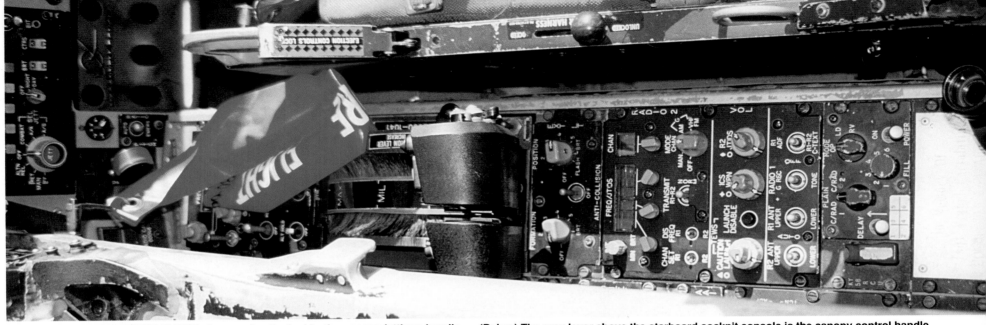

(Above) A REMOVE BEFORE FLIGHT streamer is attached to the canopy jettison handle above the port console. Below the folded streamer are controls for the Instrument Landing System (ILS) and Tactical Air Navigation (TACAN). Both throttle levers are placed in the off position. The two round buttons on the inboard throttle surface were for the microphone (upper) and speed brake (lower). Aft of the throttle quadrant are controls for exterior lighting, integrated communications, and TEWS. The white panel at the rear reads In Memory of Tsgt Miguel Portalatia – a former crew chief. (Lou Drendel)

(Below) The gray lever above the starboard cockpit console is the canopy control handle, used to raise and lower the canopy from inside the cockpit. Controls for the oxygen supply (port) and the Environmental Control System (starboard) are placed at the console's front. Gray knobs near the wall control various interior lights, while the keypad belongs to the navigation control panel. The coiled green hose supplies oxygen to the pilot's face-mask. A production ACES II ejection seat with seat edge ejection control handles is installed. (Lou Drendel)

An Air Force security policeman stands before an F-15C-35-MC (83-0017) of the 1st TFW. The Eagle has just arrived at Langley Air Force Base (AFB), Virginia from Saudi Arabia, where the Wing had deployed for Operation DESERT STORM. Capt Steve Tate flew this F-15C when he shot down an Iraqi Mirage F-1EQ in the early hours of 17 January 1991 — the opening night of DESERT STORM. (David F. Brown)

An air temperature sensor is mounted on the starboard side, aft of the nose gear door. An identical probe is mounted on the port lower fuselage side. The natural metal probe measures outside air temperatures for the engine air inlet controllers. The data ensures efficient inlet operation at all air temperatures. The port sensor also feeds information to the air data computer, which supplies data for the cockpit displays. (Lou Drendel)

The F-15C nose landing gear incorporates a taxi light (upper) and a landing light (lower). The small gear door closes with the forward-retracting gear. A larger forward gear door remains closed except for servicing and gear operation. The Goodyear tire used on F-15A through D aircraft is 22 inches (55.9 CM) in diameter by 6.6 inches (16.8 CM) wide and is inflated to 260 pounds per square inch (PSI). (Lou Drendel)

The nose landing gear steering system is automatically engaged when there is weight on the nose wheel. Electrical wiring for the taxi and landing lights run along the front of the main gear strut. Landing gear assemblies and bays are painted Gloss White (FS17875); however, the oleo (shock absorbing) strut is left in chromed natural metal for smooth operation. (Lou Drendel)

The Tactical Air Navigation (TACAN) antenna is mounted immediately aft of the F-15C's nose landing gear door hinge. This antenna receives radio navigation information from ground stations for the Litton ASN-109 Inertial Navigation System (INS). Hot air from the Tactical Electronic Warfare System (TEWS) escapes through a vent aft of the TACAN antenna. Air temperature sensors are mounted along the lower fuselage sides. (Lou Drendel)

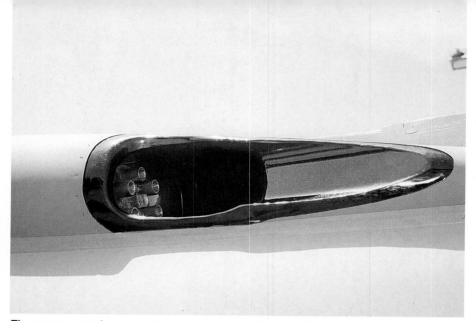

The 20MM M61A-1 Vulcan cannon is mounted inside the F-15's starboard wing root, beside the engine air intake. This position allows sufficient space for the gun and its ammunition feed system. The wing root position also prevents radar interference problems, which would result from a nose installation for the weapon. This F-15C is assigned to the 33rd Fighter Wing at Eglin AFB, Florida. (Dave Mason)

The General Electric 20MM M61A-1 is a six-barrel, hydraulically driven gun, weighing 275 pounds (124.7 KG). The weapon's selectable firing rate is either 4000 or 6000 rounds per minute. The F-15A/B/C/D carries 940 rounds for the gun, while the F-15E carries 450 rounds. The M61A-1 can fire Target Practice (TP), Armor Piercing Incendiary (API), or High Explosive Incendiary (HEI) ammunition.

The cannon muzzle aperture housing is made of titanium. This metal resists the heat from the muzzle blast. The M61A-1 Vulcan has a muzzle velocity of 3380 feet (1030.2 M) per second. The six-barrel Vulcan fires from the 3 o'clock barrel position (farthermost right). The weapon's position on the starboard wing root prevents exhaust gas ingestion by the engine air intake.

A red cover was placed over the cockpit air conditioning system exhaust duct. The cover prevents Foreign Object Damage (FOD) while the Eagle is on the ground. Below this vent on the wing glove is the cannon cooling air intake. The large vent aft on the wing glove is the cannon exhaust port. The Ultra High Frequency/Very High Frequency (UHF/VHF) radio blade antenna is mounted on the F-15C's upper fuselage. (C.M. Reed)

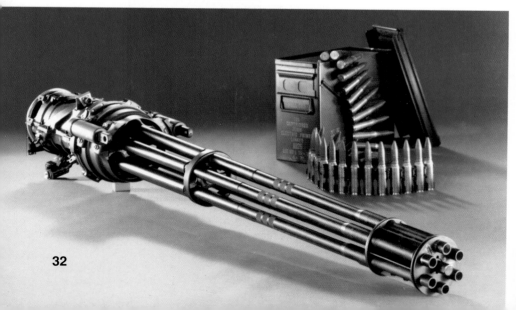

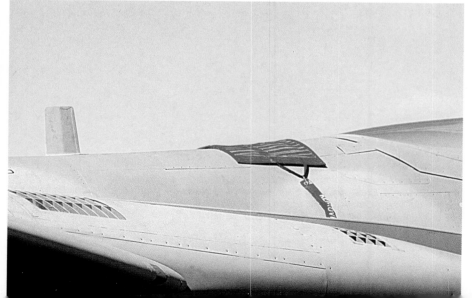

The unpainted wedge at the engine intake area allows freedom of movement for the intakes. The Eagle's intakes can pivot from -11° to +4° from the horizontal to allow efficient airflow to the engines. The insignia of the 58th Fighter Squadron, 33rd FW appears on the fuselage side. This Squadron was the highest scoring unit in DESERT STORM, accounting for 17 of the 41 Iraqi aircraft shot down by US forces. (Dave Mason)

Plate reinforcements are fitted to the port wing glove undersurface on this F-15C. The plating stiffens this wing glove area under the in-flight refueling receptacle. This is believed to be a depot level modification, since the reinforcements were not added on the production line. (Lou Drendel)

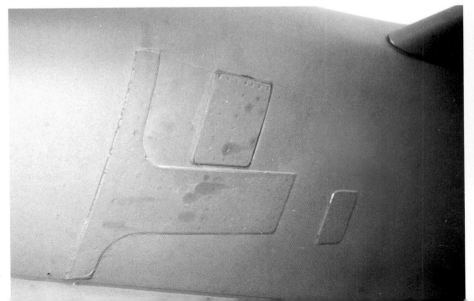

The F-15's engine air intakes are separated from the fuselage to avoid boundary-layer air, which reduces engine performance. The two ramps mounted on the intake's ceiling adjust their position in response to incoming air. These ramps control the shockwaves and ensure efficient engine operation at all angles of attack. This Eagle is fitted with a 728 gallon (2755.8 L) Conformal Fuel Tank (CFT) along the fuselage side. (Lou Drendel)

33

A bleed air duct is fitted into the outboard side of the F-15A/B/C/D engine air intake. This duct vents excess air from the intakes away from the aircraft. A depot-applied reinforcement plate was attached to the port wing glove undersurface. The slight protrusion the plating causes has a negligible effect on the F-15's aerodynamics. (Lou Drendel)

Two access panels for the 20mm M61A-1 Vulcan cannon are located in the starboard wing glove undersurface. Each panel is secured with two flush-mounted latches and opens downward on a piano hinge. Ground crews use the panels to access the weapon's breech mechanism. A red anti-collision light is mounted in the wing leading edge. (Lou Drendel)

All F-15s have red anti-collision lights mounted on the wing leading edges near the wing glove area. The pilot turns on the lights in the cockpit. These glow – except under combat conditions – to alert nearby aircraft of the Eagle's presence. The wing leading edges are fixed and lack high lift devices, such as leading edge flaps or slats. (C.M. Reed)

Four attachment points for AIM-7 Sparrow Air-to-Air Missiles (AAMs) are placed on the F-15's lower fuselage – two each on the port and starboard sides. The C-shaped ring grabs the forward missile section and secures it to the aircraft. The fore and aft attachments eject the Sparrow from the Eagle. The strake mounted above the forward attachment point section assures clean missile separation upon launch. (C.M. Reed)

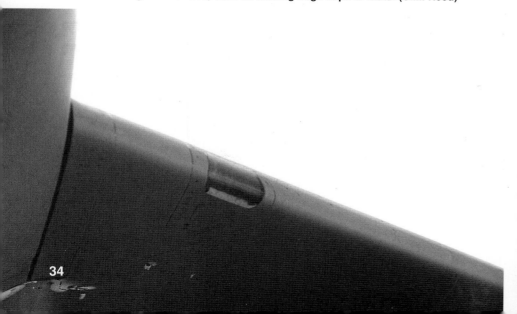

The F-15C/D main landing gear is externally identical to the earlier F-15A/B; however, the later variant's gear is strengthened to accept higher aircraft weights. The Bendix wheels are equipped with carbon heat-sink anti-skid brakes. An emergency system provides hydraulic accumulator pressure for the brakes in case the main system fails. Main landing gears and bays are painted Gloss White with chromed oleo (shock absorbing) struts. (Lou Drendel)

Eight holes in each main wheel allow cooling air to the brakes. Earlier F-15 main wheels either had 12 holes or a series of triangular openings. Main wheels were painted black until the early 1990s, when they were repainted Gloss White for improved liquid leak and wheel crack detection. The landing gear retracts forward, although only the aft gear door remains open while the Eagle is on the ground.

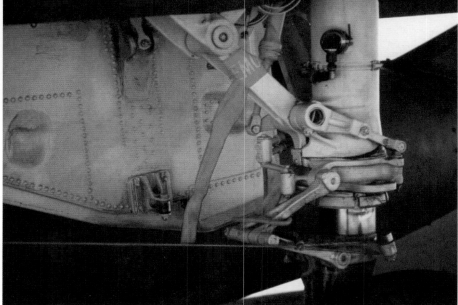

A scissor link connects the upper and lower main landing gear leg sections. The link straddles the oleo, or shock absorbing strut inside the main gear leg. The high rate of oleo compression indicates a large amount of weight on the landing gear. The actuator strut angles down from the gear bay ceiling to pull the gear up on retraction and lower the gear on extension. (C.M. Reed)

A 610 gallon (2309.1 L) fuel tank is mounted on an F-15's centerline station. The tank has two attachment lugs on the upper centerline and a pivot point on the aft rear fin. The pivot point assures a clean separation when the tank is jettisoned. The tank is rated at 9 Gs (nine times the force of gravity) when empty, allowing an F-15 pilot to retain this tank during combat maneuvers. F-15s can also carry this tank on both wing pylons. (Lou Drendel)

F-15C main landing gears are equipped with Goodyear tires, which measure 34.5 inches (87.6 CM) in diameter by 9.75 inches (24.8 CM) wide. The tires are inflated to 340 pounds per square inch (PSI). The Bendix Hydro-Air anti-skid brake system is inoperable below 30 knots (34.5 MPH/55.6 KMH) of ground speed. A red REMOVE BEFORE FLIGHT streamer is attached to the landing gear lock, which prevents inadvertent gear retraction while on the ground. (Lou Drendel)

A 33rd FW F-15C (85-0112) launches a Raytheon AIM-7 Sparrow AAM during a training exercise. The Eagle carries a 610 gallon fuel tank on the fuselage centerline. The Sparrow is a semi-active radar homing missile, which first entered service in 1956. The latest AIM-7 version is the AIM-7M, which accounted for 26 kills out of 41 total US air victories during Operation DESERT STORM in 1991. (USAF)

Light yellow electroluminescent formation lights are fitted in the F-15C's wingtips. The flush-mounted lights wrap around the wingtip to provide variable brightness levels during night and low visibility flying conditions. A fuel dump pipe is mounted on each aft wingtip beside the aileron. The pilot can dump internal fuel to lighten the aircraft for an emergency landing. (Lou Drendel)

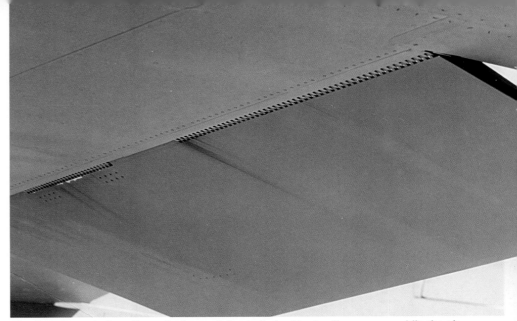

The F-15C's port wing aileron is drooped due to lack of hydraulic pressure while the aircraft is on the ground. The wing control surfaces use aluminum honeycomb construction for high strength and low weight. The plain ailerons and flaps are the only moveable surfaces on the Eagle's wing. (Lou Drendel)

The white antenna for the Loral AN/ALR-56 radar warning receiver (RWR) is mounted on the F-15's wingtip. The AN/ALR-56 detects enemy aerial and surface-based radars and warns the pilot of their presence. Immediately aft of the RWR antenna is the position light, which is red on the port wing and green on the starboard wing. (Lou Drendel)

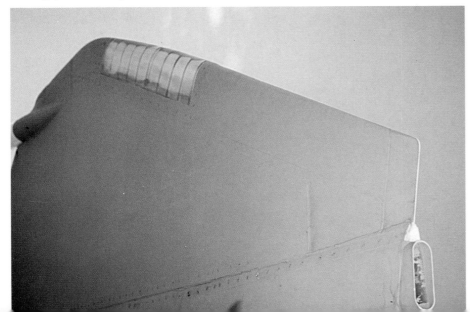

An empty LAU-114 missile launcher rail is mounted on station 8A (outboard right wing pylon) on this F-15C. The Eagle was assigned to the 57th Fighter Weapons Wing (FWW) at Nellis AFB, Nevada in 1994. The Wing teaches air combat tactics and techniques to US Air Force fighter pilots. (Lou Drendel)

An AN/ASQ-T11 and -T13 ACMI pod is mounted on station 1A on an F-15C, while an empty LAU-114 launcher rail is fitted to station 1B. AIM-9 Sidewinder or AIM-120 AMRAAMs can be mounted on the wing pylon sides. This allows fuel tanks or ordnance to be fitted under the pylon. (Lou Drendel)

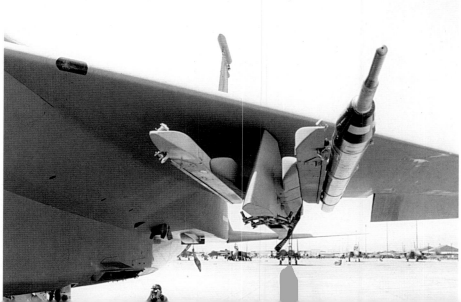

An AN/ASQ-T11 and -T13 Air Combat Maneuvering Instrumentation (ACMI) pod is installed on an F-15C's port wing pylon. The pod is mounted on an LAU-114 missile launcher rail, which is loaded onto an ADU-407/A launcher adapter. The ACMI pod provides a data link to ground stations for monitoring the aircraft's fire control system and instruments during simulated ACM flights. (Lou Drendel)

LAU-114 missile launcher rails are mounted on the sides of an F-15C's port wing pylon. An MXU-648/A travel pod is carried under the pylon. This pod holds the pilot's personal effects during deployments away from his home base. The MXU-648/A is converted from a BLU-27 fire bomb case and can hold up to 300 pounds (136.1 KG) of supplies. (Lou Drendel)

The SUU-59/A is the only wing pylon type usually carried by F-15s. A mounting bolt at the upper aft section helps secure the pylon to the wing. Midway on the SUU-59/A's side is the rear of an ADU-407/A launcher adapter. The F-15C/D has nine external stores stations and a maximum external load of 23,600 pounds (10,705 KG). (Lou Drendel)

The F-15C's starboard aft fuselage station (station 7) is one of four available stations to carry AIM-7 Sparrow AAMs. The missile is loaded onto fore and aft attachment points along the station. The AIM-7's motor ignites soon after release from the aircraft. The strake above the launch rail directs airflow to ensure positive separation when the missile is launched. (Lou Drendel)

An AIM-7 Sparrow is mounted on an F-15's starboard aft fuselage station. The Eagle is cleared to use the AIM-7E, -7F, and -7M variants. This Sparrow's body is painted flat white; most operational missiles used by F-15s are painted Light Ghost Gray (FS36375) to blend with the aircraft. The aft fuselage is left unpainted due to the heat generated by the engines. (Lou Drendel)

(Above Left) Armorers use an MJ-1 lift truck to load an AIM-7 Sparrow AAM onto a 32nd Tactical Fighter Squadron (TFS) F-15. Only the top fore and aft fins are installed on the Sparrow prior to loading on the aircraft; the other three fins per set are installed after loading. The AIM-7F/M versions are armed with an 88 pound (39.9 KG) explosive charge wrapped by a coiled steel rod, which shatters into approximately 2500 fragments on detonation. The Sparrow has a range of 62 miles (99.8 KM). The 32nd TFS deployed their Eagles from Soesterberg Air Base (AB) Netherlands to Incirlik AB, Turkey for Operation DESERT STORM in early 1991. Squadron pilots shot down four Iraqi aircraft during the conflict. (USAF)

(Above) An AIM-7 Sparrow is loaded onto the port forward fuselage station of a 27th TFS F-15C at King Abdul Aziz AB, Dhahran, Saudi Arabia during DESERT STORM. Both sets of four fins are mounted onto this missile. The Eagle is equipped with 610 gallon (2309.1 L) external fuel tanks on the fuselage centerline and under the wings for increased range. Two Ford Aerospace (formerly Philco) AIM-9 Sidewinder AAMs are mounted on the port wing pylon sides. The 27th TFS was one of two 1st Tactical Fighter Wing (TFW) squadrons to deploy from Langley Air Force Base (AFB), Virginia to Saudi Arabia soon after Iraq's invasion of Kuwait on 2 August 1990.

(Left) An AIM-9L Sidewinder is mounted on an Aero-3B launcher attached to an F-15C's port wing pylon. A yellow rubber cover is placed over the heat seeker head to protect it from damage before flight. The launcher plug is disconnected from the AIM-9L, resulting in the missile canards being displaced to their travel limit. The Eagle can carry the AIM-9J, -9L, and -9M variants of the Sidewinder. (Lou Drendel)

(Above) Two AIM-9L Sidewinders are mounted on LAU-114 missile launchers. ADU-407/A adapters provide the space between the launchers and the SUU-59/A inboard pylon. REMOVE BEFORE FLIGHT streamers are attached to the seeker head covers, which are removed prior to takeoff. F-15s are usually armed with four AIM-9s – two per wing – and four AIM-7 Sparrows or AIM-120 AMRAAMs (Advanced Medium Range Air-to-Air Missiles) on air superiority and intercept missions. (Lou Drendel)

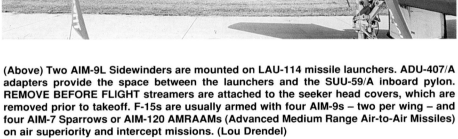

(Above Right) The AIM-9L introduced a new seeker head to the long-running Sidewinder family. The Argon gas-cooled seeker allows all-aspect target acquisition and intercept. Earlier Sidewinders were limited to tail chases due to their less capable seeker heads. The 'Lima' also includes larger canard (forward) fins of increased span over those fitted to earlier Sidewinder variants. The annular blast fragmentation warhead – a continuous steel rod wrapped around a 22.4 pound (10.2 KG) explosive charge – is fitted aft of the canard fins. (Lou Drendel)

(Right) A rolleron is fitted to each fixed aft wing on all Sidewinder variants, including this AIM-9L. Rollerons are turbines installed as free-floating ailerons and driven by the slipstream in flight. These serve to handle the missile's roll, pitch, and yaw axes maneuvers. The rollerons work with the all-moving canard fins to steady the Sidewinder's flight path towards its target. The Sidewinder's range is ten to 18 miles (16.1 to 29 KM). (Lou Drendel)

Capt Steve Tate flew this F-15C (83-0017) when he downed an Iraqi Mirage F.1 near Baghdad, Iraq on 17 January 1991. The Eagle was assigned to the 71st TFS, 1st TFW, which deployed from Langley AFB, Virginia to Dhahran, Saudi Arabia the previous August. A green star 'kill' mark was painted on the forward fuselage under the windshield. The name of Maj Mark Brugh, this Eagle's assigned pilot, is painted above the green star. (Nate Leong)

A Royal Saudi Air Force F-15C has opened its in-flight refueling receptacle door prior to coupling with the tanker aircraft's boom. The Eagle flies just below and aft of the tanker for refueling. The door is hinged at the front to expose the receptacle. All F-15s – including exports to Saudi Arabia, Israel, and Japan – can be refueled in flight.

The in-flight refueling door is flush-mounted on the F-15C's port wing glove. Louvers inboard of the receptacle door vent bleed air from the port engine air intake; identical louvers are placed on the starboard side. Immediately aft of the UHF blade antenna is the retracted speed brake, which forms the aft end of the fuselage spine. (Lou Drendel)

In-Flight Refueling Receptacle
(All F-15 Variants)

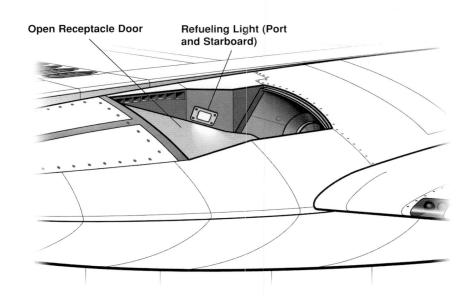

Open Receptacle Door   Refueling Light (Port and Starboard)

This 33rd TFW F-15C-39-MC (85-0102) participated in the 1988 William Tell Air Defense Weapons Competition at Tyndall AFB, Florida. A gray eagle's head is painted on a black inboard vertical tail stripe. Capt David Rose flew this aircraft when he downed an Iraqi MiG-23 on 29 January 1991, during Operation DESERT STORM. (Norman E. Taylor)

Three flush-mounted formation lights are mounted on the F-15C's aft fuselage. The pilot can adjust the pale yellow electroluminescent lights – also mounted on the forward fuselage and wingtips – for brightness. DANGER ARRESTING HOOK is painted above an arrow below the formation lights. (Lou Drendel)

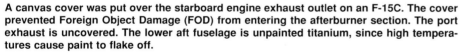

A canvas cover was put over the starboard engine exhaust outlet on an F-15C. The cover prevented Foreign Object Damage (FOD) from entering the afterburner section. The port exhaust is uncovered. The lower aft fuselage is unpainted titanium, since high temperatures cause paint to flake off.

The Pratt & Whitney F-100 engine is fitted with convergent-divergent exhaust nozzles. The nozzles' multi-flap, balanced beam arrangement allows a wide nozzle area and profile. The F-100 afterburner forward of the nozzle has five concentric spray rings in the core engine airflow and two rings slightly further downstream in the fan bypass airflow. (Lou Drendel)

The F-100-PW-220 engine powers F-15C/D Eagles delivered from October of 1986 and early F-15Es. It is 208 inches (528.3 cм) long, 46.5 inches (118.1 cм) in diameter, and weighs 3184 pounds (1444.3 кG). The -220 replaced the F-100-PW-100 of earlier F-15s. This engine was 16.8 inches (42.7 cм) shorter and 151 pounds (68.5 кG) lighter than the -220. An oil tank is mounted beside the intake. (Lou Drendel)

The F-100-PW-220 engine generates 23,450 pounds of thrust in afterburner. The earlier -100 version generated 23,830 pounds of thrust; however, the later -220 offers improved fuel economy, faster throttle response, and greater time between overhauls. (Lou Drendel)

The F-100 turbofan engine is equipped with a direct pitot-type titanium intake with a fixed nose bullet. There are 21 inlet guide vanes in a single row around the bullet. The vanes' trailing edges have variable camber (curvature) to direct the incoming air. Mounted on the bottom are the oil pump (left) and the engine alternator (alternating current electric generator). (Lou Drendel)

An F-100 engine is placed in an F-15's engine bay, with the engine face at the air intake's rear. The intake area immediately forward of the engine is painted white. This allows groundcrewmen to easily spot Foreign Object Damage (FOD) in the intake. It also eliminates the 'black hole' effect, which makes the F-15 easier to see from head-on. (Lou Drendel)

Titanium engine bay access panels – four per engine – are center hinged for easy powerplant access. The large doors allow groundcrews to perform routine maintenance on the F-100s and to make rapid engine changes. An F-15's engines can be changed within 30 minutes. (Lou Drendel)

An F-100-PW-220 engine is displayed on an engine support cart, which is used for loading and unloading powerplants from aircraft. This variant eliminated stall-stagnation problems encountered by the earlier -100 through digital engine controllers. Titanium covers (known as 'turkey feathers') covered the 17 nozzle actuators on early F-15s. The covers cost $1200 each and complicated nozzle maintenance. The 'turkey feathers' were removed with no maintenance or performance consequences. (Lou Drendel)

A red cover with a REMOVE BEFORE FLIGHT streamer is placed over the heat exchanger exhaust duct. This aft fuselage outlet lets heated air to escape from the aft avionics section. Cooling air was fed by a scoop mounted further forward under the wing. Bare titanium panels cover the engine bay. (Lou Drendel)

The Jet Fuel Starter (JFS) vent is placed on the fuselage undersurface, aft of the centerline pylon. The JFS is used to start either of the F-15's two engines, with the other engine then starting off the JFS-started powerplant. The fuselage centerline pylon is primarily used to carry a 610 gallon (2309.1 L) external tank. (Lou Drendel)

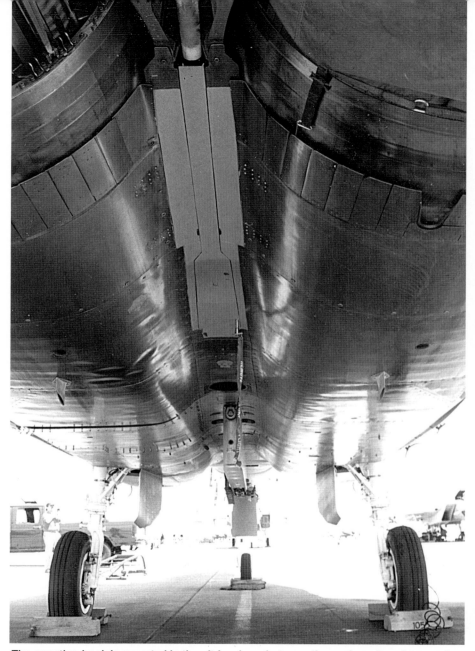

The arresting hook is mounted in the aft fuselage, between the engines. It grabs arresting cables at airfields, stopping the aircraft in the event of a brake failure. The hook extends in two seconds using gravity and hydraulic power. It hydraulically retracts in ten seconds. (Lou Drendel)

The arresting hook's aft end is enclosed within a fairing placed between the exhaust nozzles on F-15A through D aircraft. The hook is striped white and black, with the hook end left in natural metal. The door covering the hook end was deleted from F-15A/B Block 15 aircraft and removed from previous Eagles to simplify maintenance. The absence of 'turkey feathers' reveals the nozzle actuator mechanism. (Lou Drendel)

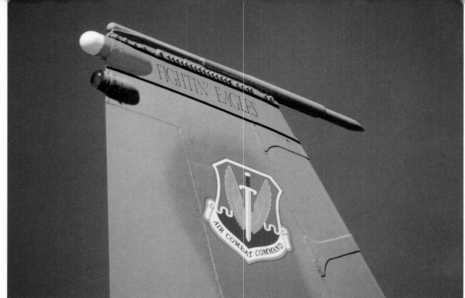

(Above) A mass balance tops the F-15's starboard vertical stabilizer. This reduces tail surface flutter from aerodynamic forces. The Loral AN/ALR-56 Radar Warning Receiver (RWR) antenna is immediately below the mass balance. A red anti-collision light is placed below the RWR. (C.M. Reed)

(Left) Groundcrewmen perform a quick starboard engine change on an F-15C (79-0074) at Lakeland, Florida in April of 1999. The Eagle is displayed at the Experimental Aircraft Association (EAA) Sun 'n Fun fly-in. This F-15C is assigned to the 58th Fighter Squadron 'Gorillas,' 33rd Fighter Wing from Eglin AFB, Florida. (Lou Drendel)

(Below) The Magnavox AN/ALQ-128 Electronic Warfare Warning System (EWWS) antenna is fitted atop the port vertical stabilizer. Below the EWWS antenna are the AN/ALR-56 RWR antenna (white) and a white position light. F-15 vertical stabilizers are built using boron-epoxy and honeycomb composite materials. (C.M. Reed)

The Northrop AN/ALQ-135 Internal Countermeasures Set (ICS) antenna is fitted to late production F-15Cs and F-15Es. The ICS actively jams guidance systems for Surface-to-Air Missiles (SAMs), Anti-Aircraft Artillery (AAA), and enemy fighters. One AN/ALQ-135 antenna is fitted on the tail and three others are mounted under the forward fuselage. (Lou Drendel)

Maintenance crews inspect a 1st TFW F-15D shortly after arriving at Dhahran, Saudi Arabia on 7 August 1990. The Eagle deployed from Langley AFB, Virginia, making a 14 hour non-stop flight requiring seven in-flight refuelings. F-15s were among the first American aircraft deployed to insure Iraq could not make air attacks on Saudi Arabia. (USAF)

The F-15D is the two-seat conversion trainer version of the F-15C and is externally identical to the earlier F-15B. A 1st FW F-15D (82-0047) flies with a restored P-51D Mustang and a 347th FW A-10 Thunderbolt II. The Mustang is marked as *Frenesi*, flown by Lt Col Tommy Hayes of the 364th FS, 357th FG during World War II. The three aircraft compose a 'Heritage Flight,' one of several which saluted the USAF during its 50th Anniversary in 1997. (USAF)

The front canopy section is identical for all two-seat F-15s (F-15B/D/E). Oils in the canopy polish cause a variety of hues. A canopy breaker is fitted to the ejection seat's headrest to shatter the canopy upon ejection if it cannot be jettisoned. The normal ejection sequence calls for jettisoning the canopy prior to flight crew evacuation. (Lou Drendel)

This F-15E-45-MC (87-0188) is deployed to Shaw AFB, South Carolina on 14 March 1990. The Eagle is assigned to the 333rd TFS, 4th TFW at Seymour Johnson AFB, North Carolina. The 4th TFW (now 4th Wing) was the first fully-operational F-15E unit. A boarding ladder is mounted on the aircraft and is used by both the pilot and the Weapons System Officer (WSO). Martin Marietta LANTIRN (Low-Altitude Navigation and Targeting, Infra-Red, for Night) pods are mounted under the engine air intakes. F-15Es are painted overall Gunship Gray (FS 36118). The fiberglass radome appears slightly darker that the rest of the airframe, probably due to a recent replacement of this part. (Norman E. Taylor)

Another F-15E-45-MC Eagle deployed to Shaw AFB is 88-1686. The aircraft is assigned to the commander of the 335th TFS, 4th TFW at Seymour Johnson AFB. White shadows are added to the black SJ tail code and to the title 335 AMU (Aircraft Maintenance Unit, which performs unit level maintenance on a squadron's aircraft). The designation 335 TFW is painted on the port vertical stabilizer. Wing insignia are applied on the starboard Conformal Fuel Tank (CFT), while squadron emblems appear to port. Another 4th TFW F-15E is parked beside 88-1686, while several A-10 Thunderbolt IIs are lined up behind the Strike Eagles. (Norman E. Taylor)

Red covers are fitted over the starboard Angle of Attack (AOA) probe (left) and the pitot tube on an F-15E. These sensors and ground covers are identical in size and position of those items found on previous F-15 variants. The Strike Eagle's Gunship Gray camouflage is designed for low visibility in low light conditions. (Lou Drendel)

The canopy is raised on *Spirit of Goldsboro*, the 4th TFW's first Strike Eagle. All F-15s use the McDonnell Douglas ACES II ejection seat. The ACES II envelope is 0 to 600 knots (690.9 MPH/1111.9 KMH) at ground level, with no sink rate. The rocket-powered ACES II gives a greatly reduced onset of G (gravity) force when fired compared to the Martin Baker seats installed in the F-4.

The first F-15E (89-0267) assigned to the 4th TFW arrives at Seymour Johnson AFB in December of 1988. It is named *Spirit of Goldsboro*, in tribute to the North Carolina city nearest the base. The Wing's three Tactical Fighter Squadrons (334th, 335th, and 336th) transitioned from F-4E Phantom IIs to F-15Es.

A pitot tube is mounted low on the F-15E's port nose; an identical tube is fitted to starboard. The probe – used to gather airspeed data – is left unpainted to prevent any interference with data collection. Electrical heating elements in the pitot probe melt ice, which can result in false instrument readings. The UHF (Ultra High Frequency) radio antenna is placed on the centerline. (Dave Mason)

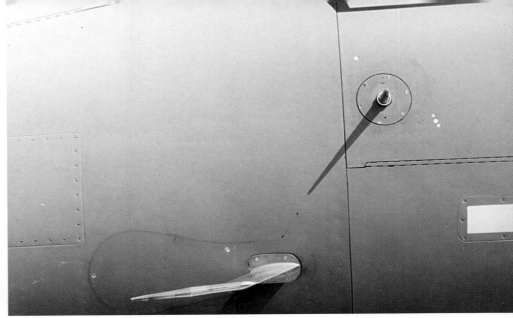

An ARMAMENT panel is placed on the F-15E's port nose, immediately aft of the radome. Armorers use this panel to indicate with a washable marker the weapons load carried on specific missions. The ARMAMENT panel appears on all USAF combat aircraft, including all F-15 variants. (Dave Mason)

The F-15E's Angle of Attack (AOA) probe is mounted above and aft of the pitot tube on both port and starboard sides. Input collected by the two AOA probes is displayed in the cockpit and warns the pilot when the aircraft stalls. Stalling occurs when an aircraft has insufficient speed at a high AOA, causing the aircraft to lose control and lift. (Dave Mason)

The F-15E uses the same forward fuselage night formation strip lights mounted on previous Eagles. The forward set is placed on the avionics bay access door. The door's piano hinge is above and parallel to the lights, while three flush fasteners are placed near the door's lower edge. (Dave Mason)

The internal access ladder is extended from the port forward fuselage. Tape covers the step control button above the ladder, preventing air show spectators from accidentally retracting the item. The retractable ladder is seldom used, in favor of an external crew ladder. (Lou Drendel)

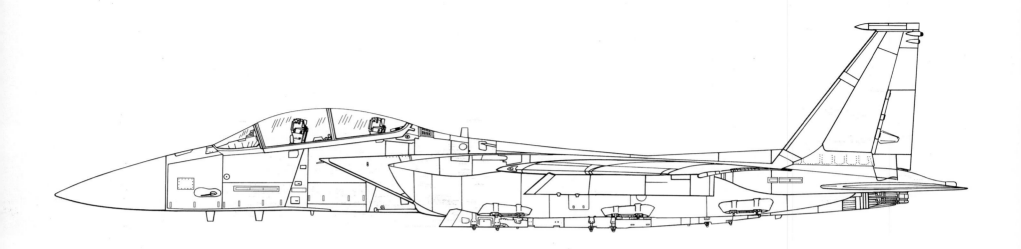

McDonnell Douglas (now Boeing) F-15E Eagle Specifications

Wingspan:..............42 feet 9.75 inches (13 м)
Length:...................63 feet 9 inches (19.4 м)
Height:....................18 feet 5.5 inches (5.6 м)
Empty Weight:........31,700 pounds (14,379.1 кG)
Maximum Weight:..81,000 pounds (36,741.6 кG)
Powerplant:............Two 23,450 pound thrust Pratt & Whitney
                      F-100-PW-220 afterburning turbofan engines
Armament:.............One 20мм M61A-1 Vulcan cannon with 450
                      rounds; up to 24,250 pounds (10,999.8 кG) of
                      external ordnance

Maximum Speed:....1650 мРН (2655.3 кмн) at 36,000 feet
                      (10,972.8 м)
Service Ceiling:.....60,000 feet (18,288 м)
Range:....................2878 miles (4631.6 км) with external fuel tanks;
                      3570 miles (5745.2 км) with Conformal Fuel
                      Tanks
Crew:.......................Two

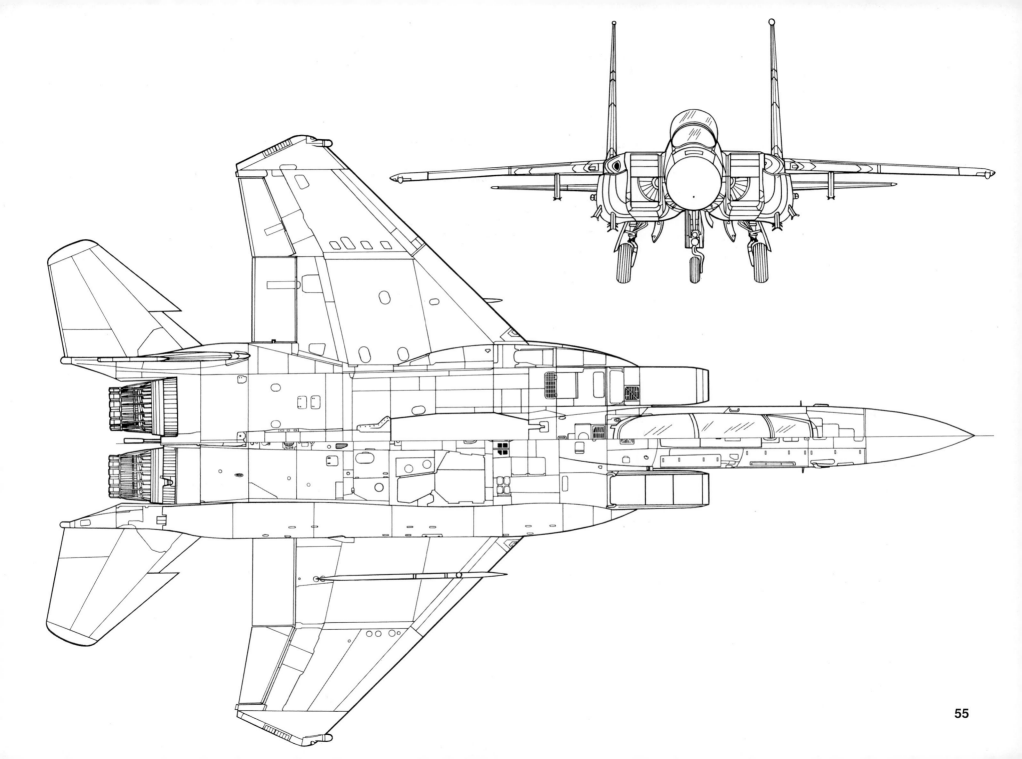

The F-15E uses the same birdstrike-resistant windshield fitted to previous Eagles. Two layers of fusion bonded cast acrylic surround a center polycarbonate layer. The HUD (Head-Up Display) combining glass is mounted on the instrument shroud and extends almost to the windshield edge. (Dave Mason)

A gun camera is mounted immediately ahead of the HUD combining glass. It records on videotape images of air-to-air and air-to-ground combat. The images are used to confirm 'kills' and to evaluate weapons and tactics. Gun cameras are also used in training exercises to evaluate the flight crew's performance. (Dave Mason)

An F-15E (87-0188) of the 461st Fighter Squadron, 58th Fighter Wing performs an in-flight refueling on 21 April 1994. This Eagle was formerly assigned to the 333rd TFS, 4th TFW. The Weapons Systems Officer (WSO) focuses on the refueling boom, which is reflected in the canopy, while the pilot forms on the tanker. The Wing is based at Luke AFB, Arizona and serves as the Strike Eagle Replacement Training Unit (RTU). Pilots and WSOs assigned to fly F-15E are trained by the 58th FW prior to their posting to operational units. (Ted Carlson/Fotodynamics)

The F-15E's HUD combining glass is larger than those found on previous Eagle variants. This larger size reflects the Strike Eagle's night/all-weather capability. The 25° by 40° combining glass displays essential flight and target information to the pilot. Up-front controls under the HUD activate various avionics equipment. (Dave Mason)

The pilot's instrument panel uses two Kaiser Multi-Purpose Displays (MPDs) on the port and starboard sides of the cockpit. The monochromatic (single-color) MPDs show weapon information and flight sensor data and video. Twenty pushbuttons around each MPD control the type of information shown. Analog flight instruments are retained for backup use. (Lou Drendel)

A Sperry Multi-Purpose Color Display (MPCD) is mounted below the up-front controls. Sensor and weapons video with overlays of symbols, advisory readouts, and navigation data are shown in either multi-color or monochromatic video. The engine monitor indicator starboard of the MPCD replaces several analog engine monitoring instruments. The throttle quadrant is placed on the port console, outboard and aft of the ejection seat control handle. Black fur seat covers are placed on this production ACES II. (Lou Drendel)

The canopy is raised on an F-15E-45-MC (88-1686) assigned to the 4th TFW from Seymour Johnson AFB, North Carolina. It was displayed at Shaw AFB, South Carolina on 13 March 1990. The aft canopy section features a slight outboard bulge, which provides additional headroom for the WSO. The starboard nameplate below the windshield names the aircraft's crew chief and assistant crew chief. The port nameplate lists the pilot and WSO.

An eagle's head outline is placed on the nameplate's leading edge. A Martin Marietta (now Lockheed Martin) AN/AAQ-13 LANTIRN (Low-Altitude Navigation and Targeting, Infra-Red, for Night) navigation pod is installed on the starboard fuselage station. The AN/ALQ-14 targeting pod is mounted on the port side. The 4th TFW insignia is applied to the conformal fuel tank, under and aft of the 20mm cannon aperture. (Norman E. Taylor)

Four 90th FS, 3rd Wing F-15Es – led by 90-0238 –are parked at Elmendorf AFB, Alaska during the summer of 2001. Crew access ladders are attached to the canopy sills. The Strike Eagles are equipped with LANTIRN pods under the engine intakes and Conformal Fuel Tanks (CFTs) along the fuselage sides. Six weapons pylons are tangentially (in-line) mounted on each CFT. Tangential carriage reduces the drag imposed by Multiple Ejector Racks (MERs) used by other USAF tactical aircraft and extends the F-15E's operating radius by up to 40 percent. A Hughes/Raytheon AIM-120 AMRAAM (Advanced Medium Range Air-to-Air Missile) is mounted on the wing pylon. (Lou Drendel)

An AIM-120 AMRAAM is mounted on an F-15E's starboard pylon outer section. The 350 pound (158.8 KG) missile can be launched from rails normally used by AIM-9 Sidewinders, as well as from the AIM-7 Sparrow launchers along the lower fuselage. Active radar homing allows the AMRAAM to be a 'fire and forget' missile, without the need for the parent aircraft's radar to continually 'paint' the target until impact. (Lou Drendel)

A red brace is manually installed to keep the F-15E canopy open for extended periods. It is removed before canopy closing. The metal hand grip bar above the instrument shroud aids in entering and exiting the aircraft. Orange covers are fitted over the pitot sensing inlets of the rear ACES II ejection seat. These inlets collect air data to determine the post-ejection automatic separation of the crewman from his seat. (Lou Drendel)

The Weapons System Officer (WSO) ejects before the pilot in an emergency. This allows the pilot to maintain aircraft control and prevents the seats from colliding outside the aircraft. Removable black fur seat covers are fitted to some F-15Es. The covers provide added comfort to the crew. (Lou Drendel)

The warning light panel above the aft cockpit CRTs alerts the WSO to aircraft systems malfunctions. Light gray pushbuttons surrounding each CRT control the type of data presented on screen. On/off switches are mounted on the upper right CRT frame, while brightness and contrast switches are placed on the lower left and lower right corners, respectively.

The WSO's instrument panel is dominated by four Cathode Ray Tubes (CRTs). Two monochromatic Multi-Purpose Displays (MPDs) are flanked by Multi-Purpose Color Displays (MPCDs). Basic flight controls allow the WSO to fly the F-15E if the pilot was incapacitated. An up-front control panel for various avionics systems is mounted starboard of the CRTs. (Lou Drendel)

Instruments under the CRTs are (left-right): cabin pressure altimeter, standby airspeed indicator, standby attitude indicator, standby altimeter, fuel quantity indicator, and clock. A vertical velocity indicator is mounted below the attitude indicator. The cockpit cooling and pressurization outlet is located on the lower center panel.

Circuit breaker panels are mounted along the starboard aft cockpit wall. The canopy control handle is forward of the circuit breakers. A hand controller for sensor operation is mounted on the starboard console; another controller is located on the port console. The Olive Drab (FS34087) oxygen hose lays over a black utility light. (Dave Mason)

Circuit breakers are also installed along the port aft cockpit wall. A padded armrest is placed on the console beside the wall. Controls for sensors, the intercommunication system, and electronic warfare equipment are installed next to the armrest. Beside the yellow ejection control handle is the port hand controller for operating sensors and cockpit displays. The throttle quadrant is placed between the hand controller and the cockpit wall.

A flight crewman walks on the port intake ramp of an F-15E. His right foot is just above the intake bleed air louvers, from which excess air is vented from the intake trunking. The crewman's left foot stands on the intake bypass air spill duct, which vents air from above the upper intake ramps. This controls the inlet duct Mach number, ensuring a subsonic airflow into the engines. (Lou Drendel)

Like previous F-15 variants, the F-15E has a large air duct immediately aft of the canopy. The duct vents air from aft cockpit avionics equipment. A different Ultra High Frequency (UHF) radio blade antenna from one used on earlier F-15s is mounted between the duct and the speed brake. The UHF antenna is a light gray, compared to the overall Gunship Gray aircraft finish. (Lou Drendel)

The F-15E nose landing gear is strengthened to cope with greater operating weights than on previous Eagles. A small taxi light is mounted on the actuator strut, above the landing light. The Michelin tire measures 22 inches (55.9 CM) by 7.75 inches (19.7 CM) and is inflated to 305 PSI. The aft door raises with the gear leg, while the forward doors open only during gear cycles. (Lou Drendel)

The nose landing gear door hinges to close forward on gear retraction. A lip at the lower door surfaces provides a resting place for the forward gear door's aft edge when these are closed. The black stenciled advisory on the door covers ground towing safety procedures. It refers to a Technical Order (TO) regarding this matter. (Lou Drendel)

This Strike Eagle's Technical Data Block (TDB) is painted on the port forward intake. The aircraft is an F-15E-49-MC, the 49 standing for the 49th F-15E production block from McDonnell Douglas (MC). The serial number (90-0227A) is prefaced by the Fiscal Year (1990) the aircraft was ordered. The A suffix refers to the Air Force. The primary jet fuel grade (JP-4) and the relevant TO are specified. (Lou Drendel)

Vinyl intake covers were placed on this F-15E-45-MC (88-1686), assigned to the commander of the 334th TFS, 4th TFW on 22 May 1991. The aircraft is marked with 52 mission markings – some hidden by the AOA sensor cover – from the Persian Gulf War. The 334th did not participate as a unit; however, some aircraft and crews were transferred to the 336th, the first squadron to achieve Initial Operating Capability (IOC). (Norman E. Taylor)

A manual precheck valve is placed on the forward end of each Conformal Fuel Tank (CFT). The normal setting prevents ground refueling of the CFT, while the lockout position allows ground refueling. All fuel tanks – six internal, three external, and two CFTs – can be ground refueled through a single pressure refueling point on the fuselage undersurface, aft of the engine intakes. (Lou Drendel)

The first F-15E received by the 4th Tactical Fighter Wing (now 4th Wing) was 87-0178, which was delivered to the unit at Seymour Johnson AFB on 29 December 1988. The blue, green, and yellow outboard tail band represents (respectively) the 335th, 334th, and 336th Tactical Fighter Squadrons. The 336th was the first Squadron to reach IOC, achieving this milestone while deployed on Operation DESERT SHIELD in 1990.

This F-15E is assigned to the 58th Tactical Training Wing at Luke AFB, Arizona. Light yellow formation strip lights are fitted to the wingtips. A navigation light (green to starboard, red to port) and a white AN/ALR-56 radar warning receiver antenna are fitted to the forward wingtip. An MXU-648/A travel pod is mounted under the starboard wing pylon. (Lou Drendel)

An F-15E-45-MC (88-1685) of the 461st FS, 56th FW flies under and aft of a tanker while on a mission from Luke AFB, Arizona on 21 April 1994. Vents on the upper engine intake surfaces and starboard wing glove are the same as for previous F-15 variants. The fiberglass radome has a fresher finish than the rest of the airframe, indicating a recent replacement of this section. (Ted Carlson/Fotodynamics)

The port wing root and anti-collision light of an F-15E. The same red light is also mounted in the starboard wing root. The light and its position are unchanged from previous Eagles. A rubber seal separates the Conformal Fuel Tank (CFT) from the airframe. It prevents air from seeping through and causing possible CFT separation in flight. (Lou Drendel)

The F-15E upper wing and fuselage surfaces are virtually identical to those found on the F-15A through D aircraft. The in-flight refueling door is outlined in white with white alignment markings ahead of the door. These markings assist tanker boom operators in finding the Strike Eagle's receptacle during night refueling operations. (Dave Mason)

The CFT's leading edge closely fits the F-15E's wing glove. These tanks slide onto rails mounted on the Eagle's intake trunks. Two bolts secure the CFT to the fuselage side. Fuel and electrical connections along the CFT's upper edge automatically mate with the fuselage connections. Each F-15E CFT holds 728 gallons (2755.8 L) of fuel. The two CFTs add 1456 gallons (5511.5 L) to the F-15E's 2019 gallon (7642.7 L) internal fuel load. (Lou Drendel)

Martin Marietta (now Lockheed Martin) LANTIRN (Low-Altitude Navigation and Targeting, Infra-Red, for Night) pods are normally mounted under the F-15E engine intakes. The AN/AAQ-13 navigation pod is placed under the starboard intake, while the AN/AAQ-14 targeting pod is on the port side. The AN/AAQ-13 includes a Forward Looking Infra-Red (FLIR) sensor above a Terrain Following Radar (TFR). The FLIR displays a video image of the terrain on the pilot's Head-Up Display (HUD). This allows high speed and low altitude flights at night under clear weather conditions. The Ku-Band TFR allows low altitude flying in bad weather conditions. The AN/AAQ-14 targeting pod includes a missile boresight correlator, which is used to guide Hughes AGM-65 Maverick Air-to-Surface Missiles (ASMs). The pod also has a laser designator for use with Laser Guided Bombs (LGBs). Red plastic covers are placed over the engine intakes. The 90th Fighter Squadron insignia is painted on the Conformal Fuel Tank. This unit – nicknamed 'Pair-O-Dice' – is assigned to the 3rd Wing at Elmendorf AFB, Alaska. (Lou Drendel)

An air scoop is mounted on the AN/AAQ-13 navigation pod's aft section. The scoop feeds air to the environmental control unit, which keeps the pod's operating temperatures within acceptable limits. An anti-FOD (Foreign Object Damage) cover is fitted over the scoop opening when the aircraft is on the ground. (Dave Mason)

An air vent is placed in the AN/AAQ-13's aft end. It allows heated air to escape from the pod, reducing the temperatures generated by the FLIR and TFR equipment. A similar grill with air scoops is mounted on the AN/AAQ-14 targeting pod aft section. (Dave Mason)

Each F-15E CFT is equipped with three BRU-46/A bomb racks. Three large circles on the outboard surface are cartridge retainers. These hold explosive cartridges, which cleanly separate weapons from the BRU-46/A. Three BRU-47/A bomb racks are mounted on the CFT inboard surfaces. (Lou Drendel)

An SUU-20B practice bomb dispenser is mounted on an F-15E's centerline pylon. The SUU-20 holds six 3 pound (1.4 KG) BDU-33 practice bombs, each with similar ballistic features to the 500 pound (226.8 KG) Mk 82 general purpose bomb. Front openings are provisions for 2.76 inch (70MM) practice rockets, which are seldom used on SUU-20s. (Dave Mason)

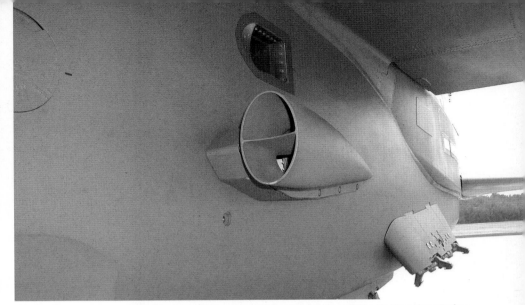

Air intake scoops are fitted to the CFT's aft section. It brings cooling air into the engine compartment. Heated engine compartment air is vented from the aircraft through the red-outlined vent above the scoop. The aft BRU-46/A bomb rack is mounted aft and below the scoop. (Lou Drendel)

The AN/AAQ-14 targeting pod to port and the AN/AAQ-13 navigation pod to starboard flank the centerline SUU-20 dispenser. The centerline pylon includes a pivot at the rear mounting point. This pivot is designed so the pylon separates down and away from the fuselage when jettisoned. (Dave Mason)

The F-15E main landing gear doors include outward bulges. These bulges accommodate the Strike Eagle's larger tires and wheels. A maintenance placard is fixed to the landing gear door to aid groundcrews working on the aircraft. F-15E landing gears and gear bays are Gloss White (FS17875). (Lou Drendel)

F-15E main landing gears are equipped with Michelin Air-X radial tires. These tires measure 36 inches (91.4 CM) by 11 inches (27.9 CM) and are inflated to 305 pounds per square inch (PSI). The wheels have eight round holes to allow cooling air into the Bendix anti-skid brakes surrounding the strut base. (Dave Mason)

The F-15E main landing gear is strengthened to accept higher aircraft weights, but is virtually identical in appearance to the F-15C/D main gear. The actuator strut assembly includes lightening holes to reduce its weight, yet maintain strength. This strut pulls the gear up and forward for retraction and pushes the gear down on extension. (Dave Mason)

Two Air-to-Air Missiles (AAMs) are mounted on an F-15E's port wing pylon. An AIM-9L Sidewinder is carried inboard while an AIM-120 AMRAAM (Advanced Medium-Range Air-to-Air Missile) is fitted to the outboard rail. AIM-9 and AIM-120 combinations are frequently found on USAF Eagles. (Lou Drendel)

This F-15E is loaded with an AIM-9 Sidewinder on the wing pylon outboard station and an AGM-130 rocket-boosted bomb under the pylon. The AGM-130 features a rocket motor underneath a GBU-15 guided bomb, which combines a 2000 pound (907.2 KG) Mk 84 bomb with a Maverick ASM seeker head and wings. Rocket power increases the bomb's stand-off range. (Lou Drendel)

The AIM-120 AMRAAM mounted on this F-15E retains the light gray body intended for use with air superiority aircraft. Blue bands indicate this is an inert missile used for training. Live missiles have a yellow warhead band in front of the forward fins and brown rocket motor bands on the aft body. The AIM-120 has a 40 pound (18.1 KG) blast fragmentation warhead and a range of 20 miles (32.2 KM). (Lou Drendel)

Insert CBU-87 cluster bombs are hung from an F-15E's Conformal Fuel Tank (CFT) pylons. The Aerojet Ordnance CBU-87 Combined Effects Munition (CEM) has 202 BLU-97/B bomblets, which are dispensed at a preset altitude using a proximity fuse. Each bomblet combines anti-armor shaped charges, a fragmentation case, and incendiary capability. (Lou Drendel)

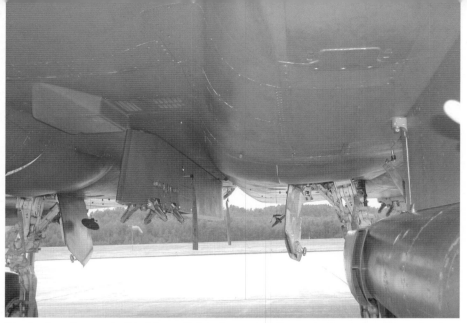

The heat exchanger is fitted immediately forward of the centerline pylon. The pylon has two pairs of sway braces mounted on its forward half. These braces prevent ordnance from swaying on the pylon before release from the aircraft. The main landing gear doors open inward to accommodate the tires and wheels. (Lou Drendel)

Covers are placed on the Tracor AN/ALE-45 countermeasures dispensers, which are mounted on the lower starboard engine nacelle. The covers are removed when the system is in use. The AN/ALE-45 can dispense up to 240 chaff cartridges for deceiving radar-homing missiles and up to 120 flares to counter heat-seeking missiles. (Lou Drendel)

A heat exchanger is placed on the centerline, between the engine nacelles. Air heated by mid-fuselage electrical equipment vents from the exchanger's aft end. Grated openings allow heated air to escape from the engine bays, reducing temperatures inside these areas. The small Doppler antenna aft of the heat exchanger constantly measures the aircraft's altitude and feeds this information to the navigation system. (Lou Drendel)

The F-15E – like previous Eagles – uses a Jet Fuel Starter (JFS) generator to start one of the F-100 engines. The JFS exhaust is located aft of the centerline pylon. Between the pylon and the exhaust is the PUSH access panel for the fire extinguisher. It puts out fires in the engine bay and the Airframe Mounted Accessory Drive (AMAD), where the JFS is connected. (Lou Drendel)

The F-15E has a strengthened arresting hook for emergency landings at greater airframe weights than for previous Eagle variants. The tailhook fairing between the engine exhausts was deleted on the Strike Eagle. An arrested landing can be made at up to 150 knots (172.7 MPH/278 KMH) of ground speed, depending upon the aircraft's weight and the arresting system in place. (Lou Drendel)

The first F-15 Eagle delivered to the US Air Force's Tactical Air Command (TAC) was this TF-15A (later redesignated F-15B; 73-108). The aircraft was delivered to Luke Air Force Base (AFB), Arizona in 1974. The original Air Superiority Blue scheme applied to F-15s was flat (FS35450) on the upper surfaces and glossy (FS15450) on the undersurfaces.

This F-15A (76-0022) flew with the 318th Fighter Interceptor Squadron (FIS) at McCord AFB, Washington State in 1984. The Compass Ghost Gray color scheme was adopted by air superiority F-15s from 1975. It was overall Light Ghost Gray (FS36375), with Dark Ghost Gray (FS36320) over parts of the upper surfaces and sides.

F-15A/B/C/D Upper Surface Finish

F-15A number 646 was assigned to the 'Twin Tails' Squadron of the Israel Defense Force/Air Force (IDF/AF) in 1989. The name *Ra'am* (Thunder) was painted in Hebrew script on the nose. This fighter shot down four Syrian aircraft in combat over Lebanon and Syria.

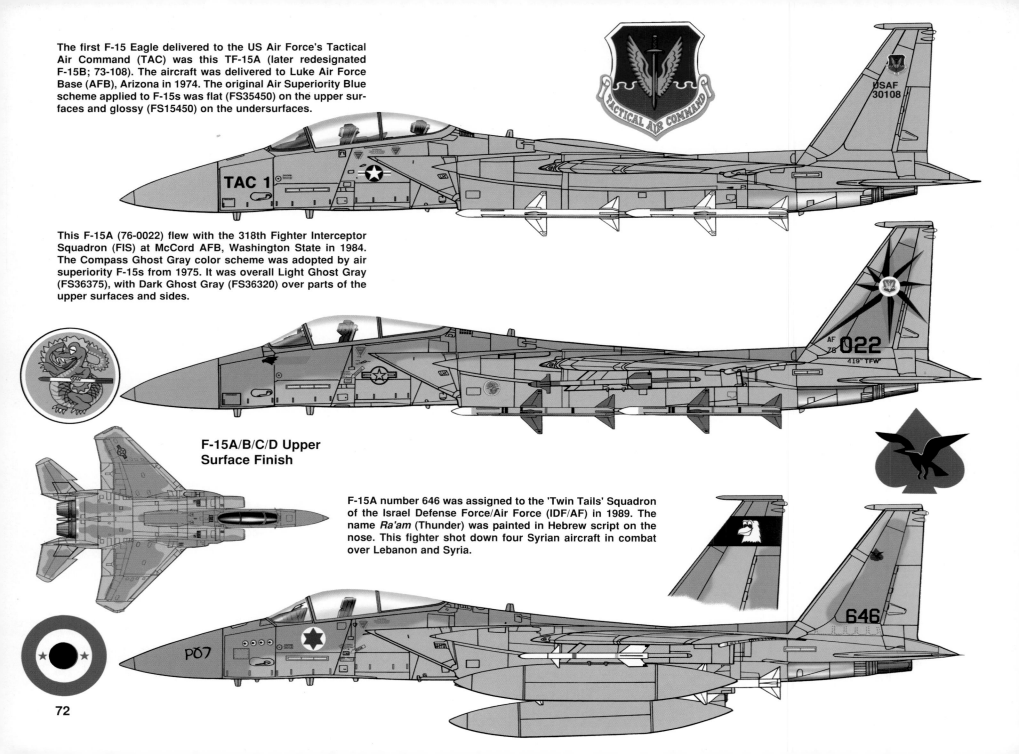

This F-15A (76-0030) is assigned to the commander of the 131st Tactical Fighter Wing, Missouri Air National Guard (ANG). The unit operates from Lambert-St. Louis International Airport – near the McDonnell Douglas (now Boeing) factory where the Eagles were built.

The 199th FS of the Hawaii ANG flies this F-15A (74-112) from Hickam AFB on Oahu. Air superiority F-15A/B/C/Ds were repainted in the 'Mod Eagle' scheme during the early 1990s. This scheme consists of overall Light Gray (FS36251), with Dark Gray (FS37176) upper surface and side portions.

This F-15DJ (92-8069) is assigned to the 201st Squadron, 2nd Air Wing of the Japan Air Self Defense Force (JASDF). The unit is based at Chitose AB in northern Japan. The F-15DJ is a two-seat F-15D, which lacks some Electronic Countermeasures (ECM) equipment. The AN/ALQ-128 Electronic Warfare Warning System (EWWS) antenna is not fitted to the port vertical stabilizer. F-15DJs operate with single-seat F-15J fighters, which resemble F-15Cs in everything except ECM equipment fit.

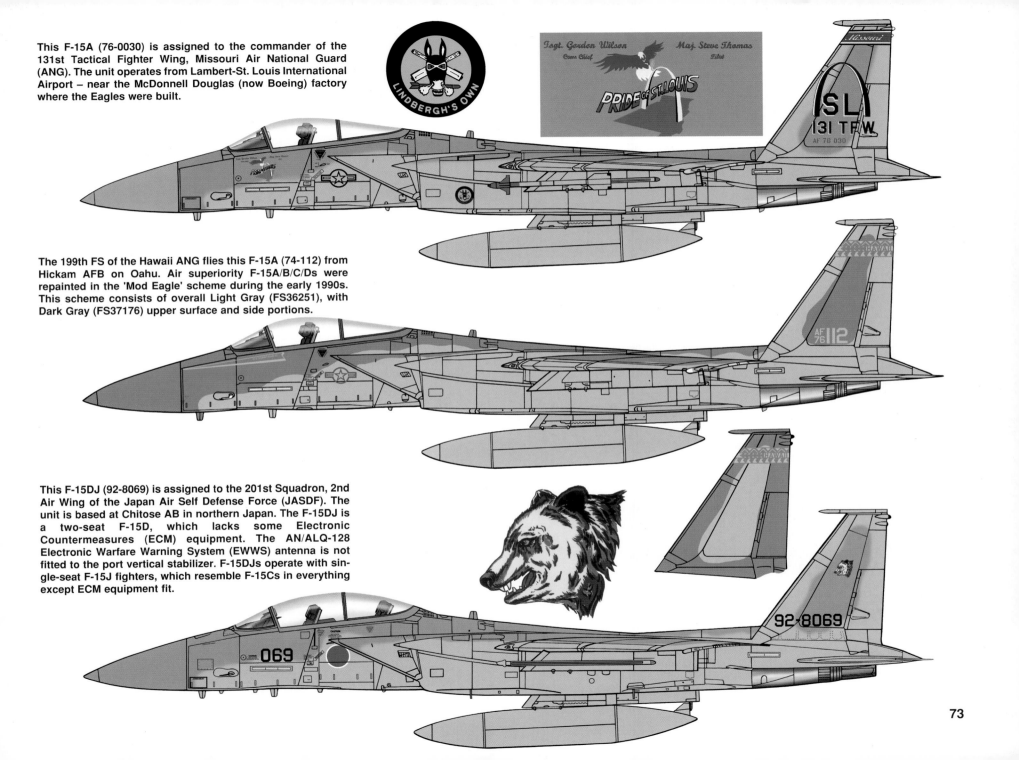

73

F-15Es have an additional strip formation light on the aft fuselage, located immediately forward of the standard Eagle strip light. This Strike Eagle is assigned to the 405th Tactical Training Wing at Luke AFB, Arizona. The base paint shop applied the PROUD EAGLE emblem to the aft fuselage boom. This area normally includes the date of painting and specified primer and top coat paints. (Lou Drendel)

Hot air exhaust ducts are mounted on the aft end of the Conformal Fuel Tanks (CFTs). The ducts allow air heated by the engines to escape from the aircraft. The normal position for this is covered by the CFTs' aft section. (Lou Drendel)

This F-15E (90-0235) bears the AK tail code of the 3rd Wing, based at Elmendorf AFB, Alaska. The red tail band with white dice represents the Wing's 90th Fighter Squadron, nicknamed 'Pair-O-Dice.' This unit is the only F-15E squadron in the 3rd Wing, which has two F-15C/D units (43rd and 54th FS). A black outline Pacific Air Forces (PACAF) insignia is painted below the tailband. A black Alaska map is painted immediately forward of the all-moving elevator. (Lou Drendel)

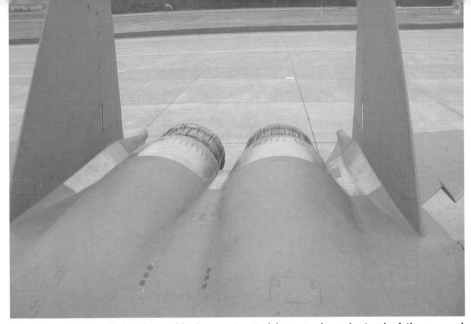

The F-15E upper aft fuselage skin is constructed in one piece, instead of the several pieces used on F-15A through D aircraft. This is possible due to using Superplastic Formed and Diffusion Bonded (SPF/DB) titanium, whose shaping qualities allow fewer parts and shorter construction time. (Lou Drendel)

F-15Es are equipped with Northrop (now Northrop Grumman) AN/ALQ-135 Internal Countermeasures Set (ICS) antennas on both tailbooms. The ICS counters enemy electronics with little effort by the F-15E's pilot. The starboard boom's square antenna is for the newer ALQ-135B band-3 ICS retrofitted to F-15Es and some F-15Cs. (Lou Drendel)

The tail of the 4th Wing Commander's F-15E-48-MC (89-0499) displays the non-standard serial presentation found on USAF unit commander's aircraft. This 334th FS Strike Eagle retains the vertical tail pods earlier F-15s use. The AN/ALQ-128 Electronic Warfare Warning System (EWWS) antenna is fitted atop the port vertical stabilizer, while the starboard tail features a mass balance. (Norman E. Taylor)

The port AN/ALQ-135 antenna has the original rounded end, instead of the chiseled end found on the later ALQ-135B band 3. The antenna's location reduces interference from engine exhaust heat, while providing full aft coverage. AN/ALQ-135 equipment is placed in the forward fuselage. (Lou Drendel)

Capt Steve Tate of the 71st TFS, 1st TFW scored the first Coalition air victory of Operation DESERT STORM. Tate flew this F-15C (82-0017) when he shot down an Iraqi Mirage F.1 at 0400 hours on 17 January 1991 – the opening night of the Persian Gulf War.

This F-15C (85-0102) was named GULF SPIRIT and assigned to the 33rd TFW from Eglin AFB, Florida. Two pilots flew this Eagle in downing three Iraqi aircraft during DESERT STORM. Capt. David G. Rose shot down a MiG-23 on 29 January 1991, then Capt. Anthony Murray downed two Su-22s on 7 February. Col Rick Parsons, Commanding Officer of the 33rd TFW, 'killed' a Su-22 while flying another F-15C (85-0124) on 7 February.

Eagle's Head on Inside Vertical Stabilizer Surfaces

The Gulf War marked the combat debut of the F-15E Eagle dual role fighter. This 'Strike Eagle' (88-1691) served with the 336th TFS, 4th TFW during the conflict and flew seven strike missions.

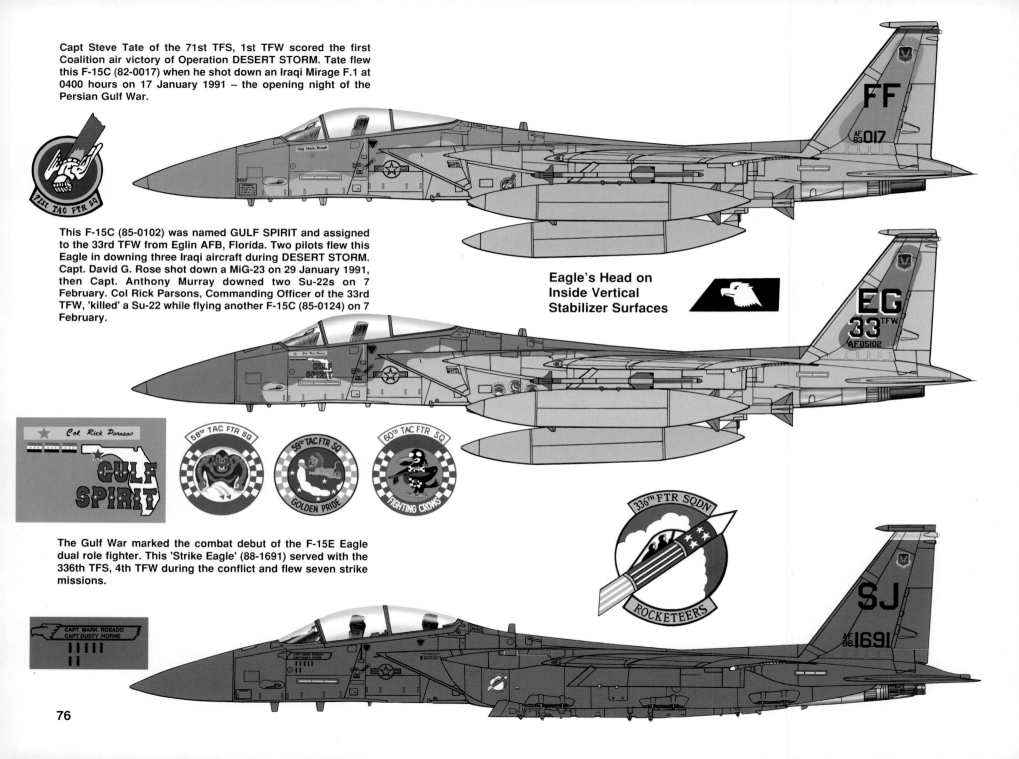

This F-15C (78-0538) was assigned to the commander of the 18th Wing at Kadena AB, Okinawa in 1993. The Wing received the first operational F-15Cs in July of 1979.

The F-15I *Ra'am* (Thunder) is the Israeli version of the F-15E Strike Eagle. Aircraft 209 is assigned to the *Patishim* (Hammers) Squadron, IDF/AF. F-15I upper surfaces are painted Tan (FS33531), Brown (FS30219), and Light Green (FS34424). The radome and undersurfaces are Light Ghost Gray (FS36375).

F-15I Upper Surface Camouflage

An F-15C (84-0014) of the 493rd FS, 48th FW downed a Yugoslav MiG-29 over Bosnia on 26 March 1999. This victory occurred during Operation ALLIED FORCE – the North Atlantic Treaty Organization (NATO) air campaign against the Serbs in Kosovo. The same Eagle shot down an Iraqi Su-22 on 20 March 1991 – soon after DESERT STORM – while assigned to the 53rd TFS, 36th TFW.

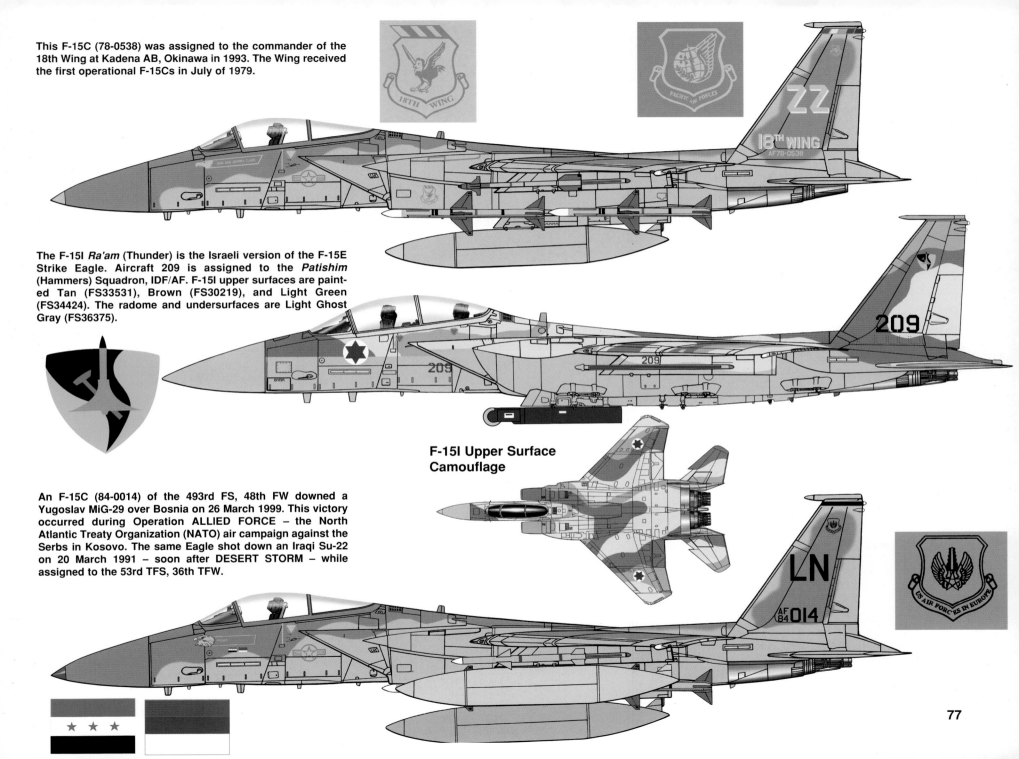

77

(Above) This F-15E-45-MC (88-1686) is assigned to the commander of the 335th TFS, 4th TFW at Seymour Johnson AFB, North Carolina. The aircraft deployed to Shaw AFB, South Carolina for a display on 13 March 1990. The tailband is blue with white trim, while the Tactical Air Command (TAC) insignia is in full color. A black diving eagle is painted on the inboard vertical tail surfaces. No ordnance is carried by the F-15E, although the LANTIRN pods are fitted. The 4th TFW insignia appears on the forward CFT area, which covers the intake trunking. The 335th TFS was the Wing's third squadron to convert from F-4E Phantom IIs to F-15Es; however, the 335th did not achieve Initial Operational Capability (IOC) until October of 1990. (Norman E. Taylor)

(Left) A 57th Fighter Weapons Wing (FWW) F-15E (86-0189) lands at Van Nuys Airport in California on 19 July 1991. The Strike Eagle deployed to Van Nuys for an open house. Aircraft of the 57th FWW wear black and yellow checkerboard tailbands. The speed brake is fully deployed at 45° to assist the F-15E in landing, while the pilot also uses aerodynamic braking. This involves holding the aircraft's nose off the runway to expose as much surface area as possible to the relative wind. The combination of the large speed brake and aerodynamic braking made incorporation of a drag parachute unnecessary in the F-15's design. The maximum flap deflection angle is 30°. (Ted Carlson/Fotodynamics)

(Above) A 335th FS F-15E-47-MC (89-0472) is decorated as the 4th FW commander's aircraft for a display at Seymour Johnson AFB on 16 October 1998. The Wing Commander's aircraft is traditionally named Spirit of Goldsboro for the North Carolina city near the base. An AIM-120 AAM is mounted on the outboard wing pylon station, with a 2000 pound (907.2 KG) GBU-84 Paveway III Laser Guided Bomb (LGB) under the pylon. Five hundred pound (226.8 KG) GBU-12A Paveway I LGBs are fitted to the CFT racks. In addition to the multicolored tail bands, this Strike Eagle's inboard vertical tail surfaces have a picture of the Wright Flyer. This refers to Kitty Hawk, North Carolina – site of the Wright Brothers' first flight on 17 December 1903. Kitty Hawk is approximately 138 miles (220.1 KM) northeast of Seymour Johnson AFB. (Norman E. Taylor)

(Right) A 57th FWW F-15E takes off in full afterburner from Nellis AFB, Nevada on 31 January 1991. The Strike Eagle is armed with 12 Mk 20 Rockeye II Cluster Bomb Units (CBUs) mounted on the CFT racks. The 7.5-foot (2.3 M) long Rockeye covers a 51,668.5 square foot (4800 M²) area with bomblets when dropped from an altitude of 500 feet (152.4 M). The wing pylons are fitted with 610 gallon (2309.1 L) fuel tanks and AIM-9 Sidewinder AAMs. (Ted Carlson/Fotodynamics)

Aircraft of DESERT STORM

In Action Series | Walk Around Series

1065 F-4 Phantom II

1095 AH-64 Apache

5506 B-52 Stratofortress

5517 A-10 Warthog

1105 F-14 Tomcat

5518 F/A-18 Hornet

1130 B-52 Stratofortress

1168 AH-1 Cobra

5519 UH-60 Blackhawk

5526 F-117 Nighthawk

from squadron/signal publications